# STAR WARS® TALES

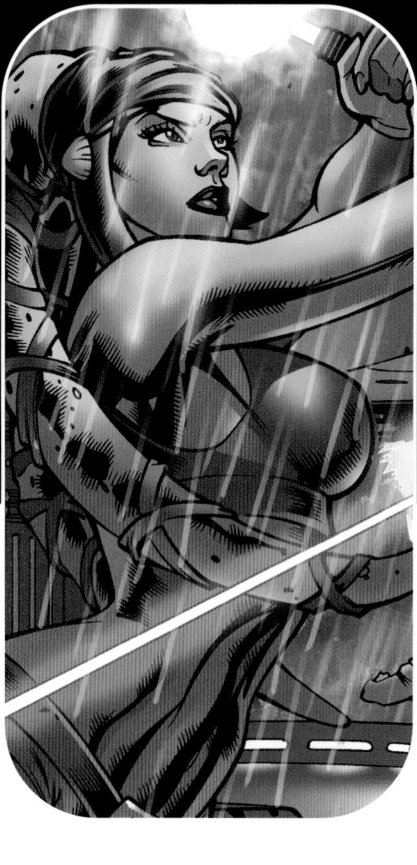

Volume 4

# STAR WARS® TALES

## CONTENTS

**Publisher** / Mike Richardson
**Editor** / Dave Land
**Editoral Assistant** / Katie Moody
**Collection Designer** / Lia Ribacchi
**Art Director** / Mark Cox

**Special thanks to**
Jonathan Rinzler **and** Amy Gary
**at Lucas Licensing**

STAR WARS®: TALES — VOLUME 4


This book collects issues 13 through 16 of the Dark Horse quarterly comic-book anthology *Star Wars®: Tales*.

Dark Horse Books™
A division of Dark Horse Comics, Inc.
10956 SE Main Street
Milwaukie, OR 97222

www.darkhorse.com
www.starwars.com

Comic Shop Locator Service: (888) 266-4226

First edition: January 2004
ISBN: 1-56971-989-6

1 3 5 7 9 10 8 6 4 2
Printed in China

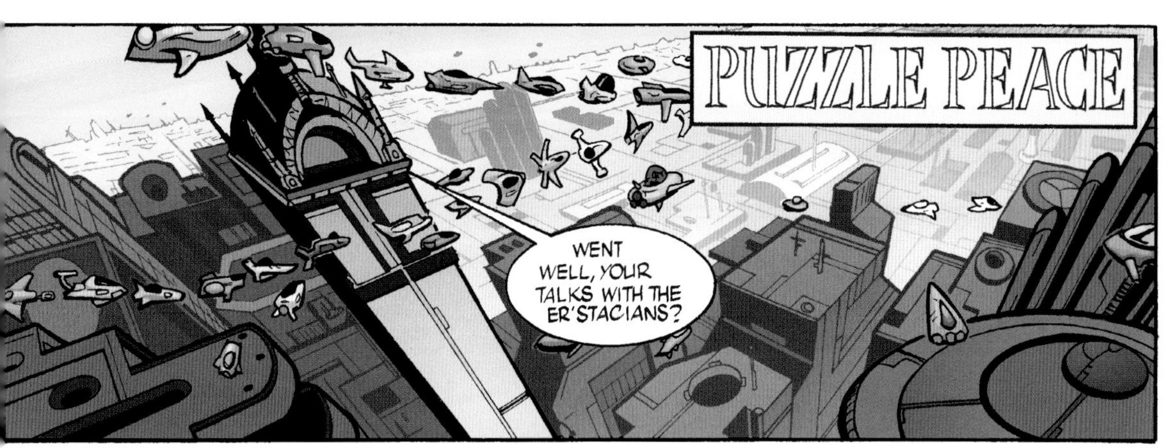

PUZZLE PEACE
WENT WELL, YOUR TALKS WITH THE ER'STACIANS?

AS WELL AS COULD BE EXPECTED.

STILL THEY QUARREL OVER THE MEGALITH?

NOT NOW.
NOT FOR A WHILE, AT LEAST.

SOLVE THEIR CONUNDRUM, DID YOU?

NO, MY FRIEND.
I LEFT THEM TO ASSEMBLE THEIR OWN SOLUTION.

"ER'STACIA LIES BEYOND THE GALACTIC RIM.
"THE ER'STACIANS THEMSELVES ARE SEPARATED ALONG CLAN LINES FROM LINEAGES BIRTHED IN GREAT TIDAL POOLS CRATERING THE PLANET.
"BUT AS YOU ARE WELL AWARE, MY VISIT THERE WAS NO DAY AT THE BEACH.
STEADY, AR-THREE.
"I WAS THERE TO AVERT GENOCIDE."
BARBAROUS.

"JEDI ARE PEACEMAKERS, ARE WE NOT?

"THE ER'STACIANS WERE TOO BUSY TEARING EACH OTHER APART TO NOTICE MY ARRIVAL.
"I QUICKLY ENGINEERED A CEASE-FIRE.
"SOME WERE NOT SO EASILY PERSUADED BY THE LESS-VISIBLE ASPECTS OF THE FORCE.
VRRMMMMZZAKT
"SO I ILLUSTRATED MY POSITION WITH COLORFUL CLARITY.
"AND THE ER'STACIANS WERE SUITABLY IMPRESSED WITH MY NEGOTIATING SKILLS."
VTOOM
AR-K-CHUK-GH!
NOW THAT I HAVE YOUR ATTENTION...

...I AM MACE WINDU, JEDI MASTER.
I HAVE BEEN DISPATCHED TO YOUR WORLD ON A MISSION OF URGENT DIPLOMACY.
THIS CONFLICT IS FINISHED.
DO NOT TEST MY PATIENCE...
...NOR THE LIMITS OF MY MERCY.
MASTER JEDI... k'tik... WE MUST RESPECTFULLY DIFFER...
...OUR DISPUTE... k'tuk... CANNOT ABATE...
...UNTIL ONE CLAN CLAIMS...
...k'tuk... THE VENERABLE ONE.

THIS SLAUGHTER IS OVER A STATUE?
OUR EXALTED ...K'TIK... MAKER.
OUR ANCESTRAL ...K'TUK... DIVIDER.
THEN PERHAPS I SHOULD DIVIDE YOUR MAKER...
...AND GIVE EACH CLAN A VENERABLE HALF?
N-N-K'TIK-K'TUK... NO!
BUT WHO WOULD CLAIM THE LONE CLAW AND ITS...K'TUK... PEARL OF WISDOM?
...OR THE UNMARRED LIMBS WITH THEIR BALANCE OF RAGE...K'TIK... AND FORGIVE-NESS?
THEN CHOOSE BETWEEN THESE HALVES.
...BUT WHO WOULD DESERVE... K'TIK... THE MAKER'S HANDSOME VISAGE... K'TIK...HIS LOVELY BARNACLED BEARD?
...OR THE SINEWY SEGMENTS WHICH... K'TUK...CARRIED HIM FROM THE PRIMORDIAL POOL TO...K'TUK...
...CONQUER THE LAND-SPACES?
OUR CLAN MUST HAVE...K'CHAK...
VTOOM

...H-HIM.
DESECRATOR!
STOP! ALL OF YOU!
BLAS... k'durk... PHEMER!
HIS SHOT WAS AN ACCIDENT!
HE DIDN'T MEAN TO HIT YOUR...
...EXALTED ONE.
A MINOR WOUND... k'tik.
BENEATH THE VENERABLE'S NOTICE... k'tuk.
GOOD ...k'tik... AS NEW.
BETTER ...k'tuk... EVEN.
UNITED WERE THEY ONLY WHEN MENDING THEIR STATUE?
PUZZLING THIS DILEMMA MUST HAVE BEEN, MASTER WINDU.
YOU HAVE NO IDEA.

"SOME KNOTS CANNOT BE UNRAVELED WITH ANYTHING BUT A BLADE.

"THE ER'STACIANS COULD NOT CHOOSE WHICH ONE PIECE WOULD SECURE A MEANINGFUL COEXISTENCE..."
V-VENERABLE...


"...SO I LEFT THEM WITH A THOUSAND CHOICES TO OCCUPY THEIR TIME."

END

THE SECRET OF TET-AMI
WITH MACE WINDU
"THE KRUY MULACKS SHOW"
LIVE FROM THE ARCHAEOLOGICAL TREASURE-TROVE OF CARTHAS-- IT'S THE "KRUY MULACKS SHOW!"
THE SOLAR SYSTEM'S MOST RELENTLESS NEWS JOURNALIST HAS COME TO UNLOCK THE TEMPLE OF TET AMI!!
HERE'S KRUUUUUUUY MULACKS!
FOR CENTURIES, THE NAME HAS BEEN WHISPERED IN HUSHED TONES.
LIVE FROM BENJA-RIHN

FOUR THOUSAND YEARS AGO, TET-AMI -- THE "TIME GUARDIAN"--
--SAVED THE ARMIES OF CARTHAS FROM A PLAGUE OF BEASTS!
AND NOW, ARCHAEOLOGISTS ARE JUST HOURS AWAY FROM TUNNELING INTO THE LONG BURIED TEMPLE ERECTED IN HIS HONOR!
WILL THEY FIND THE BODY OF THE FABLED TIME GUARDIAN HIMSELF?
OR PERHAPS THE LEGENDARY "ORB OF PASSAGE" THAT ALLOWED TET-AMI TO CONTROL TIME?

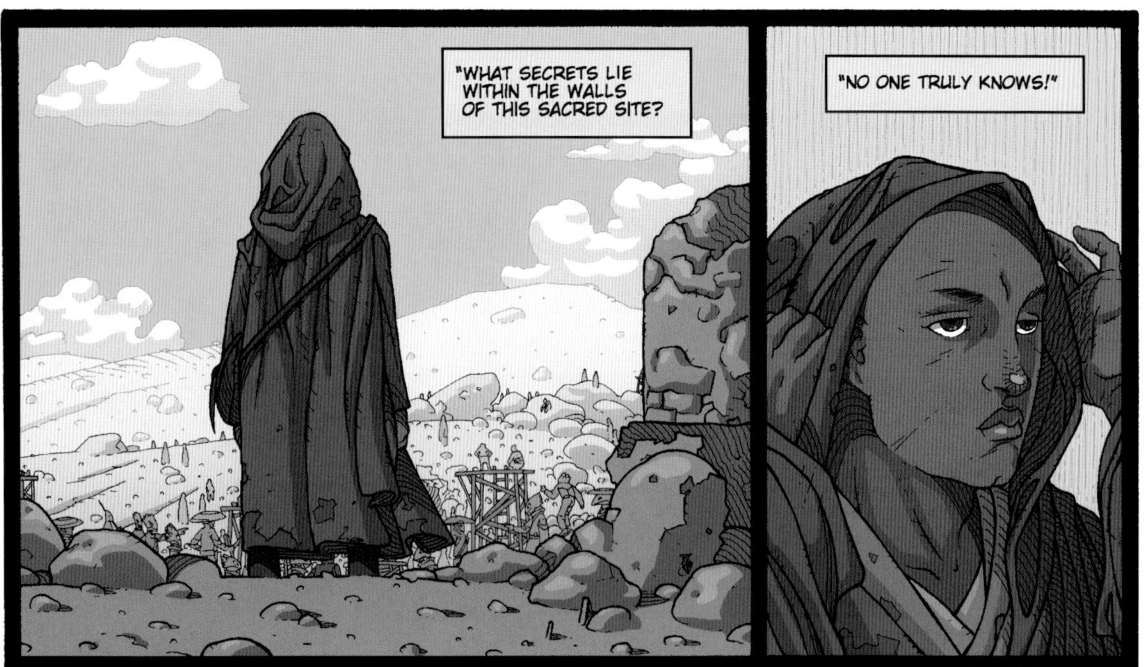
"WHAT SECRETS LIE WITHIN THE WALLS OF THIS SACRED SITE?
"NO ONE TRULY KNOWS!"

SHFF

SHUNTH

DROIDS?

THAK

VWHRRR

JVUMMM

VTT
VTT
SSSSSSS

SHRGUMMMM

?

VEEP

WHAT IS THIS MAGIC?

BROTHERS, ALERT!

GRYEEAAA

JVUMMM

FOUR DAYS LATER ...
TET-AMI!
TET-AMI!

VYYMMMYYMMMYYMMMYY
CLINK

THUNK
THUNK

WE'RE BREAKING THROUGH NOW!

CENTURIES AGO, WAS THE TEMPLE OF TET-AMI FIRST SEEN BY JEDI.

KNOW IT'S SECRETS, DID WE. PROTECT IT DID WE.
TIME PARADOX, IT WAS. HMM.

SO THE JEDI TOOK THE ORB FROM THE TEMPLE WHERE THE CARTHASIANS HAD PLACED IT-- AND SIMPLY WAITED?
AND REGENERATE IT'S TEMPORAL ENERGIES THE ORB WOULD.
UNTIL SURE WE WERE THAT MACE WINDU A JEDI KNIGHT WOULD BE.
I SEE WHY I HAD NO CHOICE BUT TO RETURN THE ORB BEFORE THE ARCHAEOLOGISTS DISCOVERED IT.

INDEED. SINCE BY YOU WAS IT BROUGHT THERE ORIGINALLY!
HMM. ALWAYS MUST A JEDI START THE JOB HE FINISHED!
END

SURVIVORS
LONG, LONG AGO AND FAR, FAR AWAY, A MAN, IF SUCH A WORD IS APPROPRIATE, OF GREAT EVIL BELIEVED HE HAD GOTTEN AWAY WITH MURDER.
DO YOU SEE HIM COMING?
NOT JUST ONE MURDER. NO, NOT JUST ONE.
"OF COURSE I CAN SEE HIM. THE QUESTION IS WHY IS HE HERE. DOES HE KNOW OF UDA-KHALID?"
"AND IF HE DOES, HOW COULD HE HAVE TRACKED KHALID HERE?"
"WHAT DOES THAT MAKE HIM, A BOUNTY HUNTER?"
"YOU KNOW THAT'S IMPOSSIBLE."

"HE CANNOT BE FOOLISH ENOUGH TO CONTINUE ON. THE WINDS ALONE WILL BE MORE THAN A MATCH FOR--"

THE EVIL DONE, THE LIVES TAKEN BY KHALID, THE SPECIES DECIMATED, BECAME LIKE INDISTINGUISHABLE WHISPERS.
THEY WERE LOST IN POLITE CONVERSATION.
LONG FORGOTTEN BY REPUBLIC AUTHORITIES.

"HE'S A HUNTER, I TELL YOU. AN EXPENSIVE ONE BY THE LOOKS OF HIM."

"YOU KNOW THAT CANNOT BE."

KHALID NEVER LEAVES SURVIVORS.

OR WITNESSES.

KHALID DOES NOT SIGN HIS ACTS OF VIOLENCE, NOR WOULD HE RISK THE SEEDS OF REBELLION THAT ARE GROWN FROM THE BLOOD OF MARTYRS.

"BUT IF HE IS A BOUNTY HUNTER, IT WILL BE UP TO US TO STOP HIM BEFORE HE REACHES KHALID."

"I THINK YOU'VE FORGOTTEN SOMETHING."

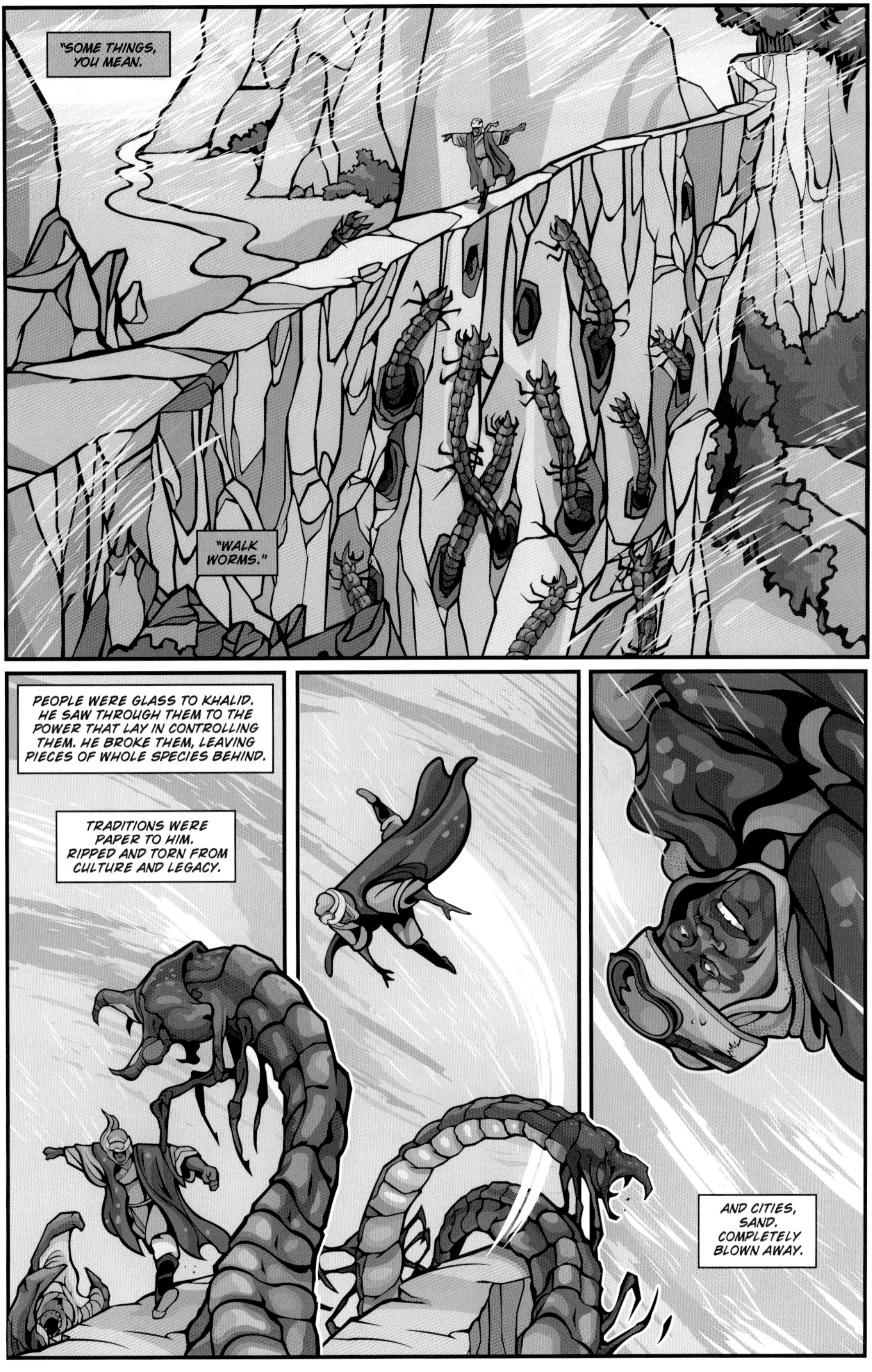

"SOME THINGS, YOU MEAN.

"WALK WORMS."

PEOPLE WERE GLASS TO KHALID. HE SAW THROUGH THEM TO THE POWER THAT LAY IN CONTROLLING THEM. HE BROKE THEM, LEAVING PIECES OF WHOLE SPECIES BEHIND.

TRADITIONS WERE PAPER TO HIM. RIPPED AND TORN FROM CULTURE AND LEGACY.

AND CITIES, SAND. COMPLETELY BLOWN AWAY.

MURDER, YES. HE HAD GOTTEN AWAY WITH MURDER.
HE HAD DEFINED IT. HE HAD GIVEN THE WORD SCOPE AND MEANING.
HE GAVE IT AMBITION.
"I'VE NEVER SEEN ANYTHING LIKE THIS BEFORE. HAVE YOU?"
"I DON'T SEE ANY WEAPONS, EITHER. DO YOU?"
"WHO COULD AFFORD A BOUNTY HUNTER LIKE THIS?"
"ALERT UDA-KHALID."
SHRUMM

DO YOU SEE WHERE HE WENT?
HE WAS CLIMBING A ROCK JUST A MOMENT AGO.
WHERE COULD HE BE?
NO! HE COULD NOT BE HERE --NOT SO SOON!

YOU GUARD THESE WALLS WELL FROM OUTSIDE INTRUDERS.
BUT I AM INSIDE THESE WALLS. THEREFORE I CANNOT BE A DANGER. AND YOUR JOB IS TO PROTECT FROM OUTSIDE INVASION.

HE'S NOT A DANGER IF HE'S INSIDE THESE WALLS. WE PROTECT UDA-KHALID FROM OUTSIDE INVASION.
STAY YOUR GROUND, KEEP YOUR EYES OPEN.

UDA-KHALID HAD BELIEVED HE HAD ESCAPED.
THERE WAS NO EVIDENCE OF WHAT HE'D DONE. NO CLUE TO TRACE HIS GUILT.
NO REASON TO SUSPECT HIM.
WHAT IS THE PRICE, BOUNTY HUNTER? HOW MUCH WERE YOU PAID FOR ME?
I COULD DOUBLE IT.
I HAVE BEEN PAID WITH THE STORY OF WHAT YOU DID. THAT IS ENOUGH.
BUT YOU SHOULD KNOW THAT I DID NOT COMMIT THE CRIMES I AM BLAMED FOR.
THERE WAS NO EVIDENCE. NONE. NO SURVIVORS. NO WITNESSES.

NONE?

NO ONE EVER GETS AWAY WITH MURDER.

"NEVER.

"YOUR VICTIMS DIDN'T HAVE TO SURVIVE TO TELL ME OF THE EVIL THAT WAS COMMITTED AGAINST THEM."

I HAVE HEARD ENOUGH, BOUNTY HUNTER.
WHO DO YOU THINK YOU ARE THAT YOU CAN JUDGE ME?

I AM ONE WITH THE FORCE.
I AM MACE WINDU, JEDI KNIGHT.

VERY WELL.

IT HAS BEEN A LONG TIME SINCE I KILLED A JEDI.

YOU LIE, UDA-KHALID!
YOU HAVE NEVER KILLED A JEDI. IF YOU HAD, WE WOULD HAVE KNOWN.

VMMM
WE ARE ALL A PART OF LIFE. THAT IS WHAT GIVES US OUR POWER. THAT IS WHAT WE SERVE.

HOW DID YOU-- I'VE NEVER SEEN-- SO FAST...

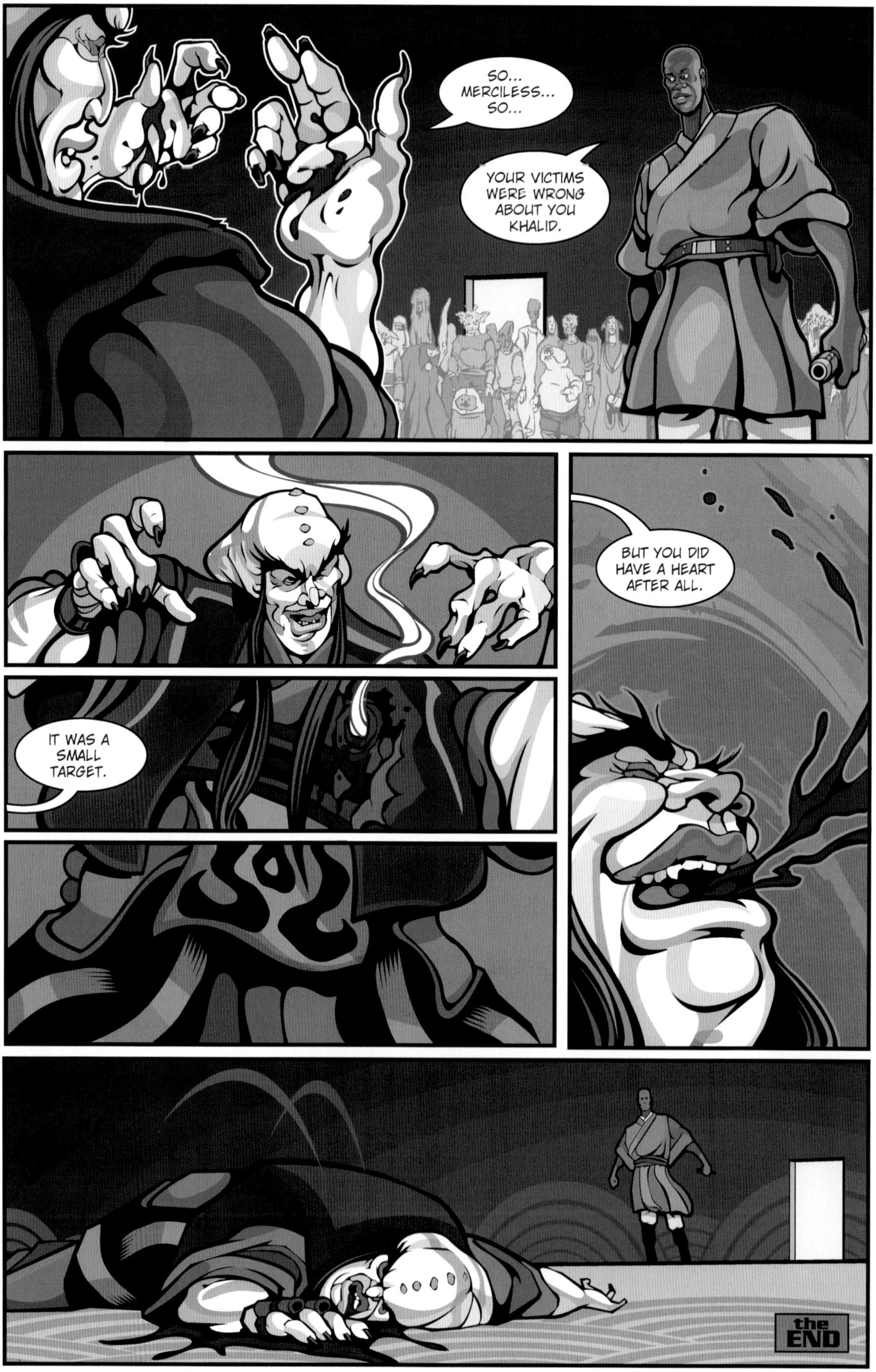

BUT YOU DID HAVE A HEART AFTER ALL.

IT WAS A SMALL TARGET.

STONES
"I ADMIT, I WAS COCKY. MAYBE EVEN ARROGANT. I WAS THE TOP OF MY CLASS...
"...BUT BY FOURTEEN, I HAD NOT YET BUILT MY FIRST LIGHTSABER.
"THAT WAS CAUSE FOR CONCERN AMONG MY MASTERS.
"THE JEDI COUNCIL SUGGESTED THAT I WAS AFRAID.
"BUT I WAS JUST LOOKING FOR THE RIGHT CHALLENGE... CRYSTALS THAT WOULD MAKE MY LIGHTSABER UNIQUE.

"SO MASTER YODA SENT ME TO HURIKANE, FAR BEYOND THE OUTER RIM.

"IT WAS MY FIRST SOLO MISSION...

"...AND I KNEW I WOULD SUCCEED."

AAAAAAARGH!
"AFTER ALL, I HAD MY WITS...

"...AND THE FORCE...

"...AND MY FEET.

"BUT, I HADN'T YET LEARNED SELF-CONTROL...

"...OR RESPONSIBILITY."

AHHHH!

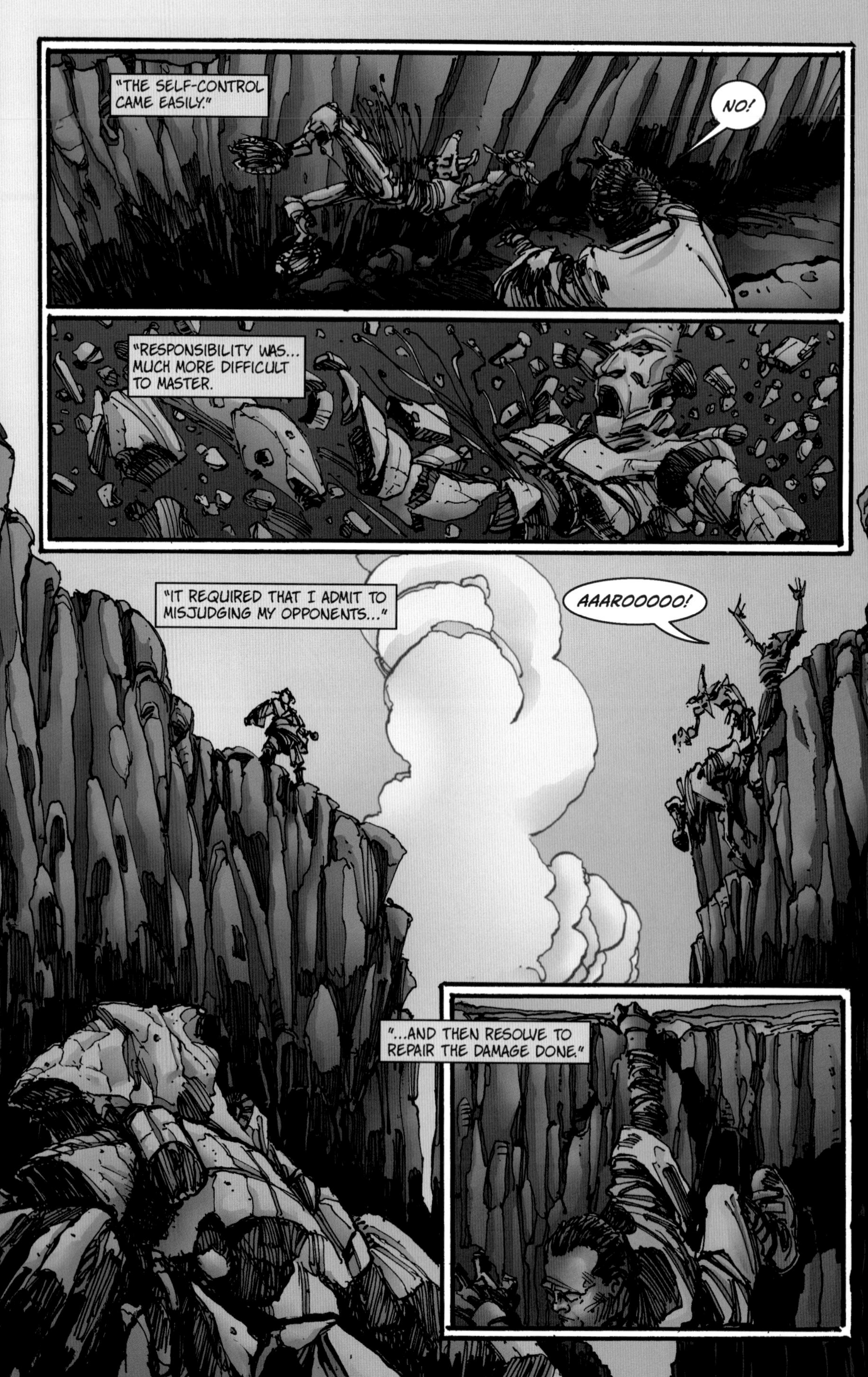
"THE SELF-CONTROL CAME EASILY."
NO!
"RESPONSIBILITY WAS... MUCH MORE DIFFICULT TO MASTER.
"IT REQUIRED THAT I ADMIT TO MISJUDGING MY OPPONENTS..."
AAAROOOOOO!
"...AND THEN RESOLVE TO REPAIR THE DAMAGE DONE."

PLEASE... LET ME HELP.
"I KNOW NOW THAT A JEDI MUST BE CONFIDENT...

"...BUT ALSO SELF-AWARE...

"...COMMITTED...

"...SELFLESS...

"ON HURIKANE, I BECAME A JEDI KNIGHT, IN SPIRIT IF NOT IN TITLE.


"AND THE REWARDS WERE GREAT."

THANK... THANK YOU.

NOW, WHO'S READY TO BUILD A LIGHTSABER?

END

The Sith in the Shadow

THOSE MARKINGS...

WHAT DO YOU SEE, PADAWAN?

"NOT JUST THE GIRL, THIS CITY... THIS PLANET! MASTER, THESE CREATURES--THEY FOLLOW THE SITH!"

PERHAPS SO. BUT FOR NOW... THEY MOSTLY FOLLOW FOOD.
A MARK ON THE SKIN AND A WISH TO SURVIVE ARE HARDLY A SIGN OF THE DARK SIDE.

BUT EVEN WITH OUR SKILLS, MASTER... WE ARE ONLY TWO, ON AN ENTIRE PLANET--
JEDI!

IF YOU CAN SENSE WHO WE ARE, EVEN IN THIS FEARFUL PLACE, THE FORCE RUNS STRONG IN YOU. LET IT ALSO TELL YOU TO HEED MY WORDS.

THIS PLANET WILL SOON DIE. YOU MUST NOT GO NOW.

AND SEEK OUT THE PART OF YOURSELF WHICH KNOWS I SPEAK THE TRUTH.

AN ANCIENT TEMPLE OF GREAT POWER IS NEARBY. SENSE ITS PRESENCE, PADAWAN.
IT IS TIME FOR YOU TO BEGIN TO LEAD.
LET US SEE HOW MUCH YOU HAVE LEARNED.

MASTER... IF YOU FEED YOUR ENEMY, DO YOU NOT STRENGTHEN HIM?
NO, PADAWAN. YOU STRENGTHEN YOUR-SELF. YOU STRENGTHEN THE FORCE. AND SO YOU BRING WEAKNESS TO THE ENEMY'S OWN DARK SIDE.

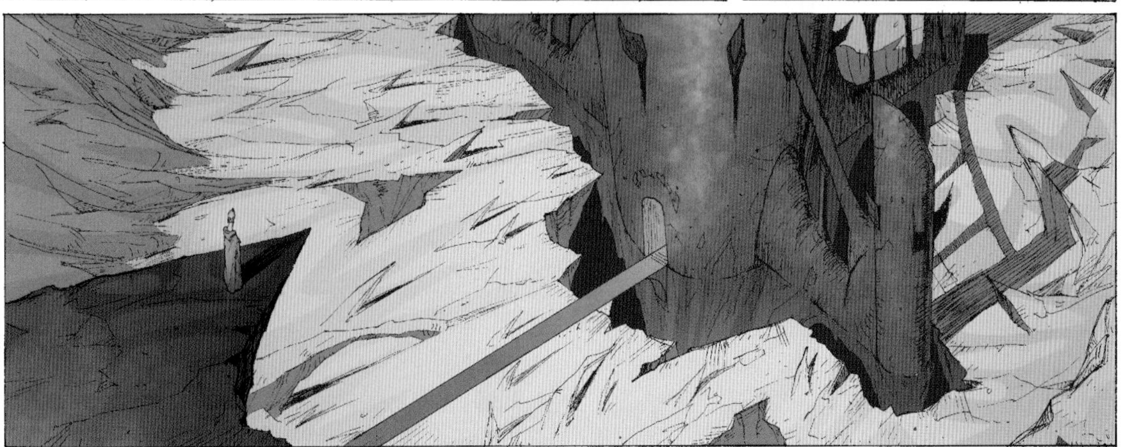

YOU HAVE DONE WELL, PADAWAN. BUT YOU MUST COMPLETE YOUR TASK QUICKLY.

MY... *TASK?*
THIS PLANET WILL NOT SURVIVE TO SEE THAT SUN RISE AGAIN, APPRENTICE.

INSIDE YOU WILL FIND, ALONE, AN ADVERSARY I HAVE FOUGHT FOR AS LONG AS I HAVE BEEN A JEDI.

THE MASTER IN THIS BUILDING HAS TRAINED MANY. HE HAS KILLED MANY.
BUT HE WILL PASS FROM THIS PLACE *BEFORE* THIS PLANET IS DESTROYED.

HOW THIS ENDS IS WHAT WE ARE HERE TO LEARN--BY THE FORCE, BY YOUR HAND, EVEN BY HIS OWN, PERHAPS.
BUT YOUR ACTIONS WILL MAKE THAT CHOICE.

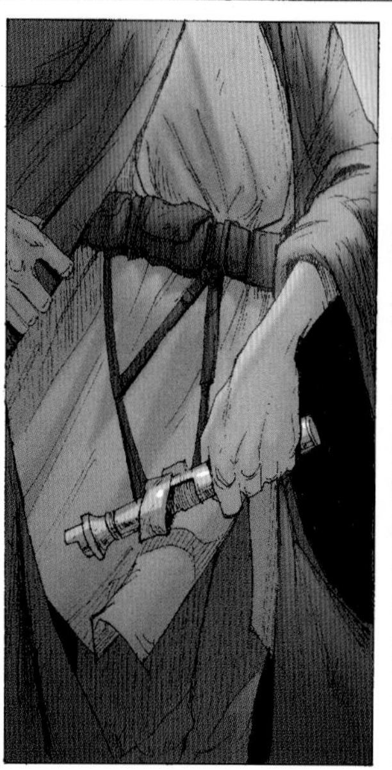

MASTER, HOW WILL I KNOW WHEN--

SKRT
SKRT
SKRT
SKRT
SKRT
SKRT

KVZZZ

KZAK

MASTER, I DON'T UNDER-STAND...

THE DARK SIDE LIVES IN THIS TEMPLE, PADAWAN, BUT NOT BECAUSE IT IS SITH. THE DARKNESS IS WITHIN *YOURSELF*.

BUT YOU SAID--
I SAID WHAT I SAID, AND IT WAS TRUE. YOU HEARD WHAT YOU HEARD, AND IT WAS FALSE.
WHY DID YOU BRING ME *HERE?!*

A SITH TEMPLE? BECAUSE THERE IS EVIL IN THE UNI-VERSE.
A DYING PLANET? BECAUSE YES, WE ALL DIE. BUT THE FORCE REMAINS.
A TRUE JEDI SERVES NOTHING ELSE...
...REGARDLESS OF TIME OR PLACE OR FEAR OF DEATH.
YES, MASTER. SO YOU HAVE TAUGHT ME.

AS I HAVE ALSO TAUGHT YOU FEAR?
WRATH? PRIDE? I HAVE TAUGHT YOU NOTHING.
I WILL LEARN--
YOUR TASK HERE IS COMPLETE. NOW WE MUST GO.

YOU HAVE *FAILED* IN YOUR TRAINING.

end

CORUSCANT--THE JEDI TEMPLE.

CHILDREN of the FORCE

WAAA!

Shhh, LITTLE ONE. LET THE FORCE CALM YOUR SPIRIT.

ARE YOU TROUBLED, MASTER WINDU?

NOTHING A LITTLE MEDITATION WON'T TAKE CARE OF.
YOU'VE DONE WELL ON YOUR FIRST **JEDI EXTRACTION,** DEPA.

THIS CHILD WILL SOON BEGIN TRAINING AS THE OTHERS HAVE--
--TRAVELING THE PATH OF THE JEDI FOR THE REST OF HIS LIFE.
AND EVENTUALLY, HE WILL BE CHOSEN AS A PADAWAN, JUST AS I CHOSE YOU.

FOR WHICH I AM THANKFUL, MASTER.
HOWEVER, THIS MISSION HAS LEFT ME WITH CONFLICTING THOUGHTS.
I WONDER IF PERHAPS IT IS CRUEL TO TAKE A CHILD AWAY FROM ITS PARENTS LIKE THIS?

A JEDI'S PATH MUST BE **SINGULAR** AND **FOCUSED.** THERE IS NO ROOM FOR **EMOTIONAL ATTACHMENTS.**
THE EDICT OF THE JEDI ORDER ISN'T ARBITRARY. IT EXISTS AS SUCH FOR A **REASON.**

I KNOW... IT'S JUST THAT...
...EVEN THOUGH I NEVER KNEW MY PARENTS, SOMETIMES I HAVE DREAMS ABOUT THEM...

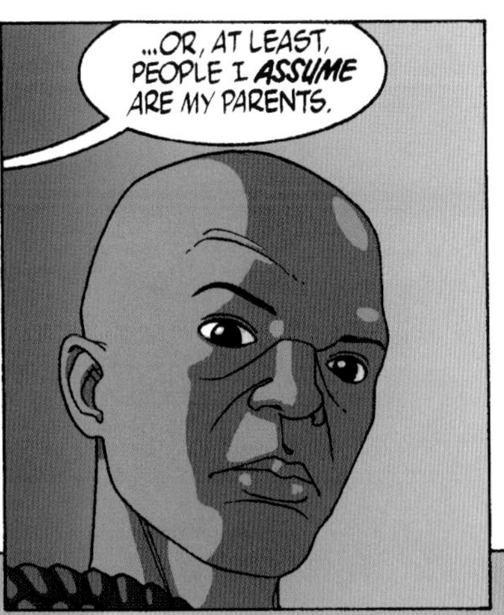
...OR, AT LEAST, PEOPLE I ASSUME ARE MY PARENTS.

DEPA, IF YOU WANT TO BECOME A JEDI KNIGHT, YOU MUST RID YOURSELF OF SUCH DISTRACTING THOUGHTS.

"THAT IS THE VERY REASON POTENTIAL JEDI ARE TAKEN AS INFANTS.

"IF WE WERE TO BEGIN TRAINING DURING ADOLESCENCE, THE STUDENT WOULD POSSESS TOO MANY CONFLICTING FEELINGS--AND THAT COULD LEAD TO THE DARK SIDE.
"OUR PURPOSE IS TO SERVE AS THE GUARDIANS OF PEACE THROUGHOUT THE REPUBLIC. BUT WE ARE FEWER IN NUMBER TODAY, SO WE MUST STRIVE TO KEEP OUR TRADITIONS ALIVE."
WE ONLY DO WHAT IS NECESSARY FOR THE GOOD OF THE GALAXY--WHAT IS RIGHT IN THE FORCE.
YOU ARE RIGHT, OF COURSE, MASTER WINDU. I CONCEDE TO YOUR GREATER WISDOM.
WISDOM CAN BEGIN WITH QUESTIONING...

click
...AS LONG AS WE LET THE FORCE GUIDE US TO THE CORRECT ANSWERS.
FZZZZZTTT

SO MANY CHILDREN...
TIK
FWISH
AAAGH!!
FFZT
FWOOSH

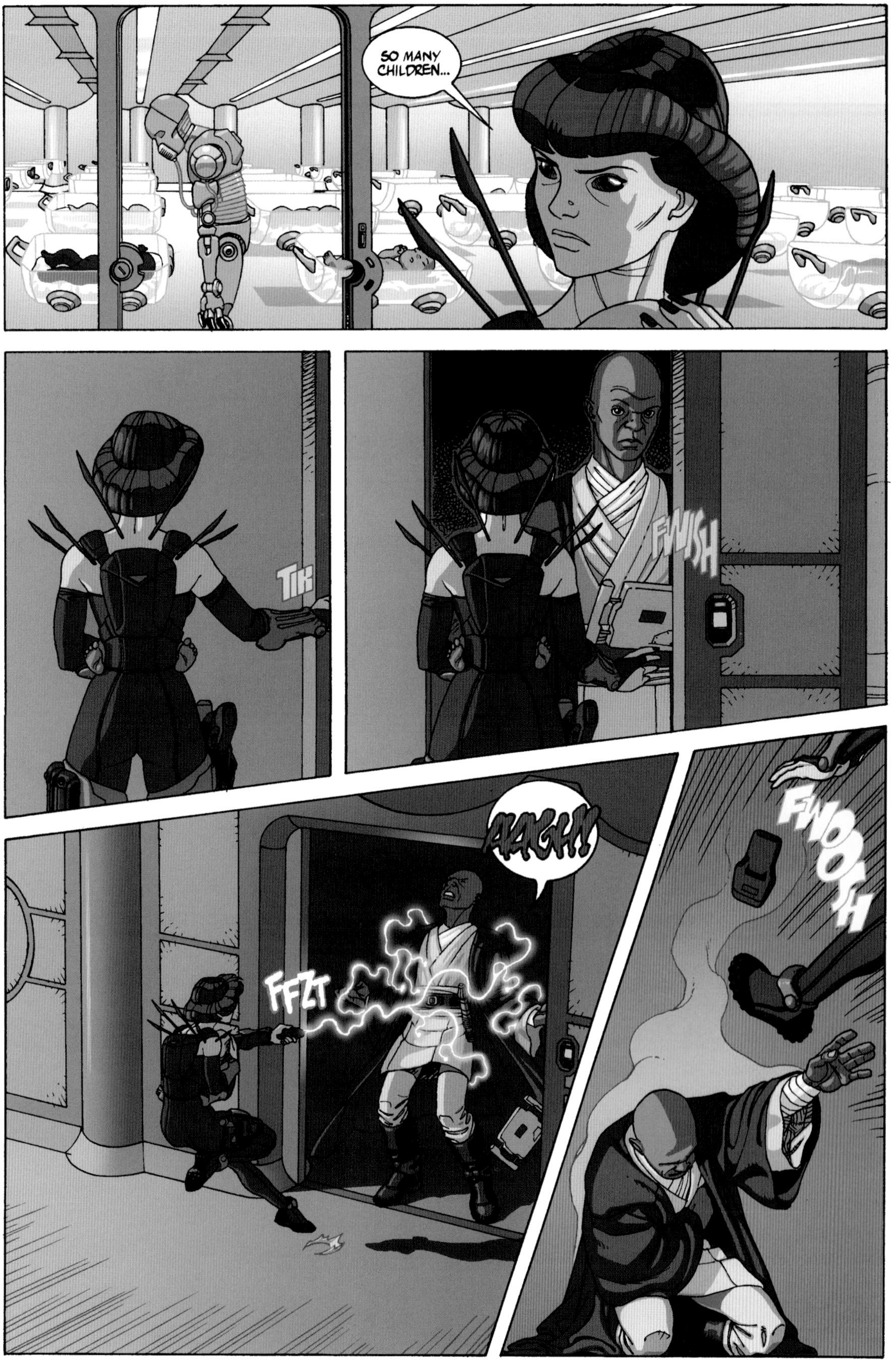

VIANNA D'POW!
UMM

I REALIZE FORCE-SENSITIVE CHILDREN BRING QUITE THE CREDIT ON THE BLACK MARKET, BUT THIS IS LOW EVEN FOR YOU.
DON'T MAKE ME DO SOMETHING YOU'LL REGRET, MACE.

I DON'T NEED THE FORCE TO KNOW THAT YOU'RE NOT ABOUT TO KILL YOUR OWN PRIZE.

BTEW
BTEW
BTEW

ZWAP

BTEW
BTEW

KRAAASSHH

ZWAP

WAAHHH!

WWWHAAAA
AAAAHH!

DO YOU HAVE ANY IDEA HOW HARD IT IS TO GET THEM TO GO BACK TO SLEEP?

THUD

CLACK

IS THIS ANY WAY TO TREAT A LADY?

YOUR **ZELTRON CHARMS** WON'T WORK ON **ME,** VIANNA.
*Ah,* THAT'S RIGHT-- A JEDI SHALL NOT KNOW LOVE...
AN ORDER OF MONKS WHOSE MOST PRECIOUS WEAPON IS THEIR ENERGY SWORD...

...A PSYCHIATRIST WOULD HAVE A FIELD DAY WITH THE LOT OF YOU.

ENOUGH.
WHO ARE YOU WORKING FOR? THE HUTTS? BLACK SUN?

YOU'VE GOT IT ALL WRONG AS USUAL, MACE. I'M NOT SELLING YOUR "FORCE-BABIES" ON THE BLACK MARKET.
I'M WORKING FOR THE KID'S PARENTS.

THEY JUST WANT THEIR BABY BACK.

THAT'S NOT POSSIBLE... IT WOULD BE TOO DANGEROUS TO RETURN THE CHILD--TRAINING HAS ALREADY BEGUN.
BESIDES... IT IS A GREAT HONOR FOR ONE'S OFFSPRING TO BE CHOSEN BY THE JEDI ORDER. IT--

WHAT GIVES YOU THE RIGHT TO CHOOSE?!
TO FORCE THESE KIDS TO ENDURE A STIFLED LIFE OF ARCHAIC TRADITIONS?

THERE'S MORE TO LIFE THAN "HONOR" AND YOUR DAMN ORDER.

...LIKE THE LOVE SHARED BETWEEN A CHILD AND ITS PARENTS.
BUT THAT'S SOME-THING YOU WOULDN'T KNOW ANYTHING ABOUT.

Hmm...
...OR MAYBE YOU UNDERSTAND AFTER ALL...

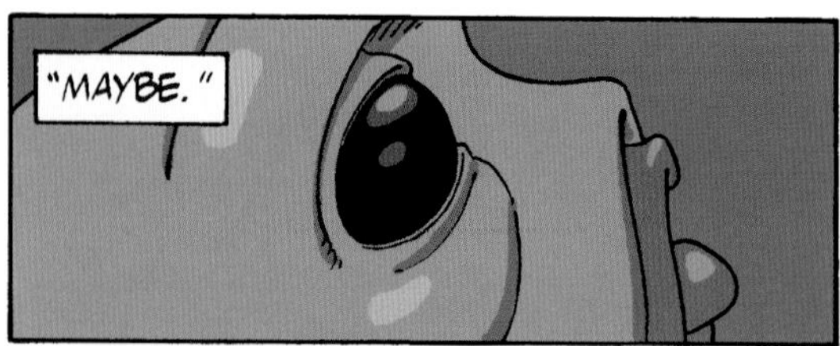
"MAYBE."

MACE-
WHILE WE KNOW WE ARE FORBIDDEN TO MAKE CONTACT WITH YOU, WE WOULD LIKE TO SEE OUR SON JUST ONCE. PLEASE.
--YOUR LOVING PARENTS

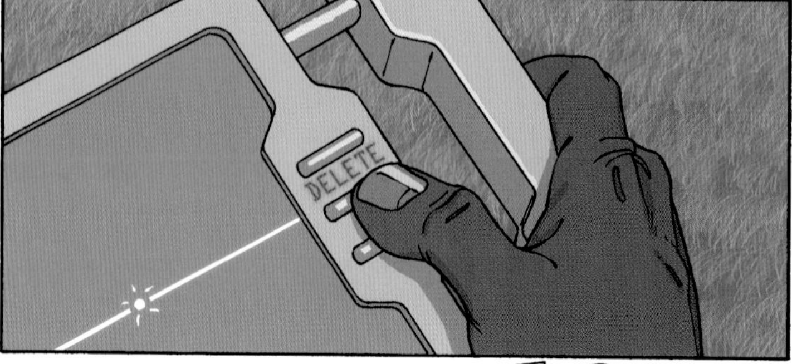
DELETE

END

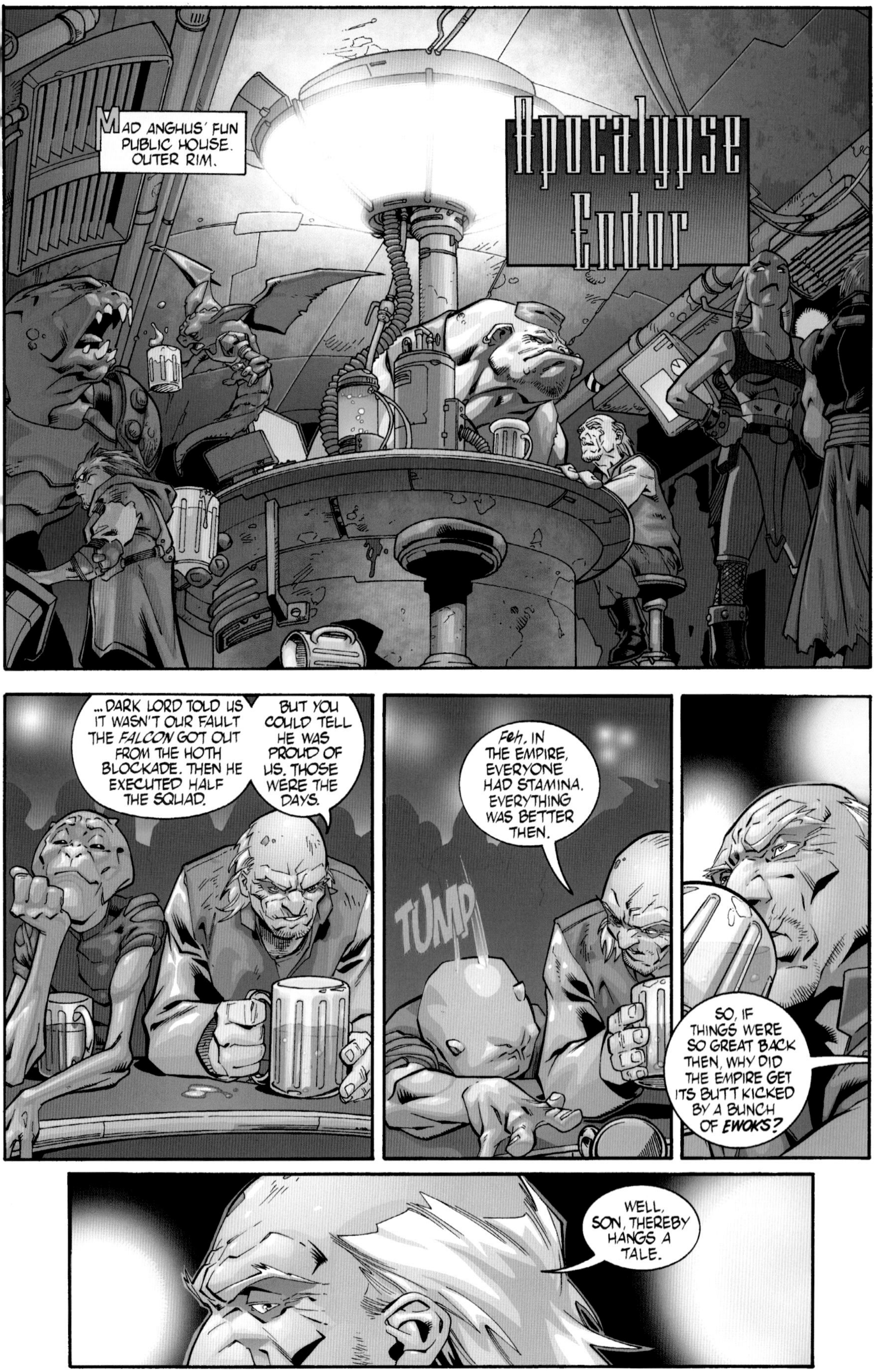

# Apocalypse Endor

MAD ANGHUS' FUN PUBLIC HOUSE. OUTER RIM.

...DARK LORD TOLD US IT WASN'T OUR FAULT THE *FALCON* GOT OUT FROM THE HOTH BLOCKADE. THEN HE EXECUTED HALF THE SQUAD.
BUT YOU COULD TELL HE WAS PROUD OF US. THOSE WERE THE DAYS.

*Feh.* IN THE EMPIRE, EVERYONE HAD STAMINA. EVERYTHING WAS BETTER THEN.
TUMP

SO, IF THINGS WERE SO GREAT BACK THEN, WHY DID THE EMPIRE GET ITS BUTT KICKED BY A BUNCH OF ***EWOKS?***

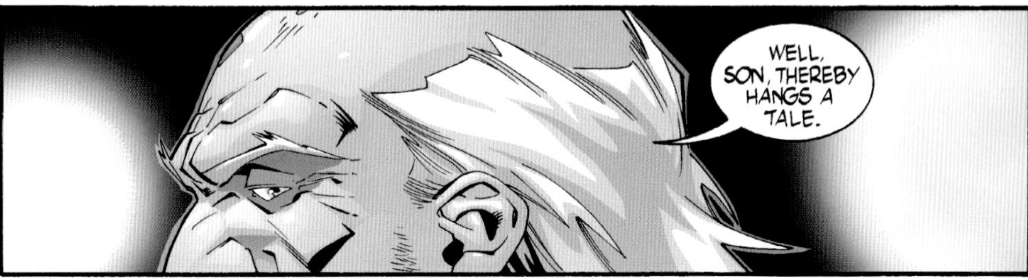
WELL, SON, THEREBY HANGS A TALE.

MY OLD MAN CALLED IT A "P.R. COUP"!
I'LL NEVER FORGET BEING A KID AND WATCHING VIDS OF THOSE CUTE, FUZZY WIDDLE EWOKS DESTROY A LEGION OF THE EMPIRE'S FINEST.
YOU GUYS HAD WALKERS, BLASTERS, ARMOR, SPEEDER BIKES, STARSHIPS. WHAT DID THE EWOKS HAVE? POINTY STICKS AND A HAPPY SONG.
THERE'S A LOT NEVER GOT SHOWN. A LOT GOING ON THOSE REBEL SCUM NEVER SHOWED ANYONE ABOUT THE EWOKS.
"WHEN WE FIRST DISPATCHED ON ENDOR WE KNEW THERE WAS A 'TRIBAL, ARBOREAL' CULTURE THERE, BUT WE WERE THE EMPIRE. WE HAD THE TECH, THE TROOPS, THE NUMBERS. WHO CARED?"
ALL RIGHT, SQUAD. WE'VE GOT TO GO MAKE CONTACT WITH THESE "EWOKS." SEE WHAT THEY'RE MADE OF.

SIR! WE'VE GOT MOTION! FIVE HOSTILES!

FORM UP, MEN, WEAPONS READY! NO FIRING UNLESS ON MY ORDER.
THIS IS FIRST CONTACT PROTOCOL.

THERE! CONTACT!

"AND THAT WAS FIRST CONTACT."

"WE WERE A LONG-RANGE PATROL. A FEW DAYS AFTER FIRST CONTACT, WE MET THOSE MONSTERS AGAIN."
...NOTHING ALL DAY.

MAYBE THEY DON'T SHOW UP ON INFRA-RED AT ALL...

GAHH!

WHERE'S KOVACS?
WHAT'S THAT SOUND?
"THAT WAS THE FIRST NIGHT WE HEARD THEIR DRUMS IN THE DARKNESS.
DOOM DOOM DOOM DOOM

"WE FOUND WHAT WAS LEFT OF KOVACS A FEW DAYS LATER. THEY'D DONE THINGS TO HIM.
"FIGURED THEY WANTED TO... TAKE HIS SPIRIT INTO THEMSELVES."

ALL THROUGH THE NIGHT WE'D HEAR THEM DRUMMING. DOOM DOOM. DOOM DOOM. WE STARTED TO GO CRAZY.

DOOM
DOOM
DOOM
DOOM
RIGHT! THAT'S IT! I'VE HAD ENOUGH OF THOSE FURRY LITTLE MONSTERS!

ZOW
ZOW
STOP IT! JUST STOP!
"EVENTUALLY, HE RAN OUT OF AMMO.

"NEVER DID KNOW FOR SURE WHAT HAPPENED TO HIM. THAT'S HOW THEY WORKED. ONE BY ONE. FROM OUT OF THE DARKNESS."

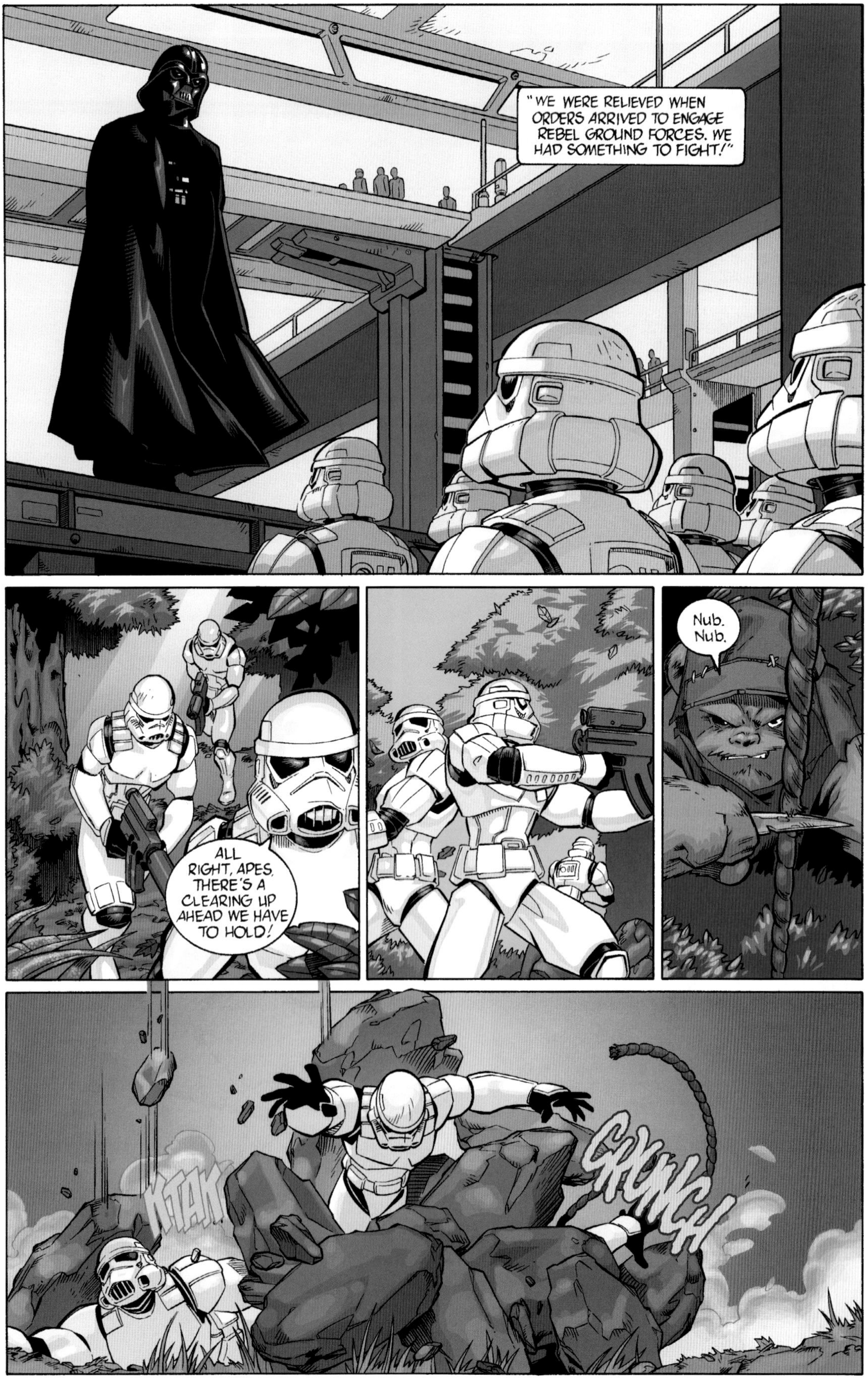

"WE WERE RELIEVED WHEN ORDERS ARRIVED TO ENGAGE REBEL GROUND FORCES. WE HAD SOMETHING TO FIGHT!"

ALL RIGHT, APES, THERE'S A CLEARING UP AHEAD WE HAVE TO HOLD!

I SEE ONE!

IEE!

SNAKT

OOF!

AAHG!

VICIOUS... LITTLE... INHUMAN...

RETREAT!

" YOU KNOW, BY THE END OF THE BATTLE..."

" ...I WAS GLAD TO BE TAKEN PRISONER BY SOLO AND THE OTHERS.

" AT LEAST A REBEL WOULD HAVE JUST SHOT YOU...

DON'T LEAVE ME, SARGE! I CAN MAKE IT, MAN!

"...NOT HAVE COME OUT OF THE TREES AND TAKEN YOU ONE BY ONE.

"BUT ONE THING KEPT ME GOING ALL THESE YEARS.
"THROUGH ALL THE BAD DREAMS THAT CHILL ME TO MY FEET.

BATTLE'S OVER.
I DON'T CARE! JUST TAKE ME HOSTAGE! KEEP THEM AWAY!
"YOU KNOW WHAT THAT IS?

"IT'S THAT WHILE I NEVER HAD A GOOD NIGHT'S SLEEP SINCE ENDOR, AT LEAST I CAN TAKE COMFORT IN THE FACT THAT WHEN THIRTY BILLION TONS OF METAL EXPLODES IN THE LOWER ATMOSPHERE OF A SMALL MOON, IT'S ONLY GOT ONE PLACE TO GO."
THAT'S A MYTH. EVERYONE KNOWS MOST OF THE DEATH STAR SIMPLY VAPORIZED, AND THE REBEL FLEET INTERCEPTED THE REST OF THE WRECKAGE.
THEY DID?
Um, YEAH.
Oh...
END

IBC BRINGS YOU THE FOLLOWING PRESENTATION...

IBC

THIS IS THE PLAINTIFF, NEELA.

SHE CLAIMS HER SON GREEDO WAS SIMPLY TRYING TO MAKE A LIVING AS A DEBT COLLECTOR...
...WHEN HE WAS KILLED IN COLD BLOOD BY THE DEFENDANT.
SHE ONLY WANTS TO SEE JUSTICE SERVED.

THIS IS THE DEFENDANT, HAN SOLO.
HE SAYS THE PLAINTIFF'S SON WAS A BOUNTY HUNTER FOR JABBA THE HUTT, WHO NOT ONLY THREATENED HIS LIFE, BUT SHOT AT HIM FIRST.

HE WAS LEFT WITH NO CHOICE BUT TO FIRE HIS WEAPON IN SELF-DEFENSE.
HE'S ACCUSED OF "BLASTING FIRST AND ASKING QUESTIONS LATER."

REAL CASES PRESENTED BY REAL LITIGANTS WHO HAVE AGREED TO HAVE THEIR DISPUTE SETTLED HERE, IN OUR FORUM--

THE EMPEROR'S COURT

ALL RISE FOR THE HONORABLE JUDGE PALPATINE.

YOU MAY BE SEATED.
THUD
ALL RIGHT, LET'S MAKE THIS SNAPPY. I'VE GOT AN ELEVEN-THIRTY APPOINTMENT TO GET MY MIDI-CHLORIAN COUNT CHECKED.

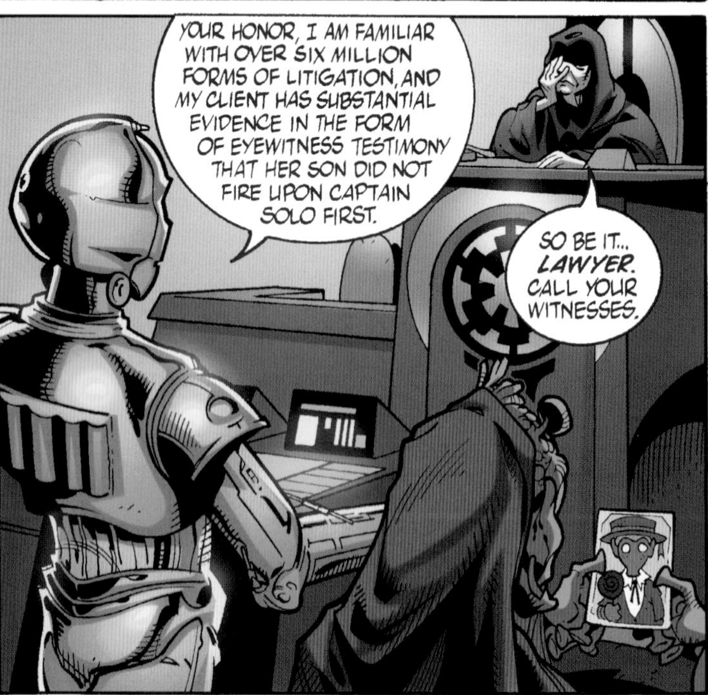
YOUR HONOR, I AM FAMILIAR WITH OVER SIX MILLION FORMS OF LITIGATION, AND MY CLIENT HAS SUBSTANTIAL EVIDENCE IN THE FORM OF EYEWITNESS TESTIMONY THAT HER SON DID NOT FIRE UPON CAPTAIN SOLO FIRST.
SO BE IT... LAWYER. CALL YOUR WITNESSES.

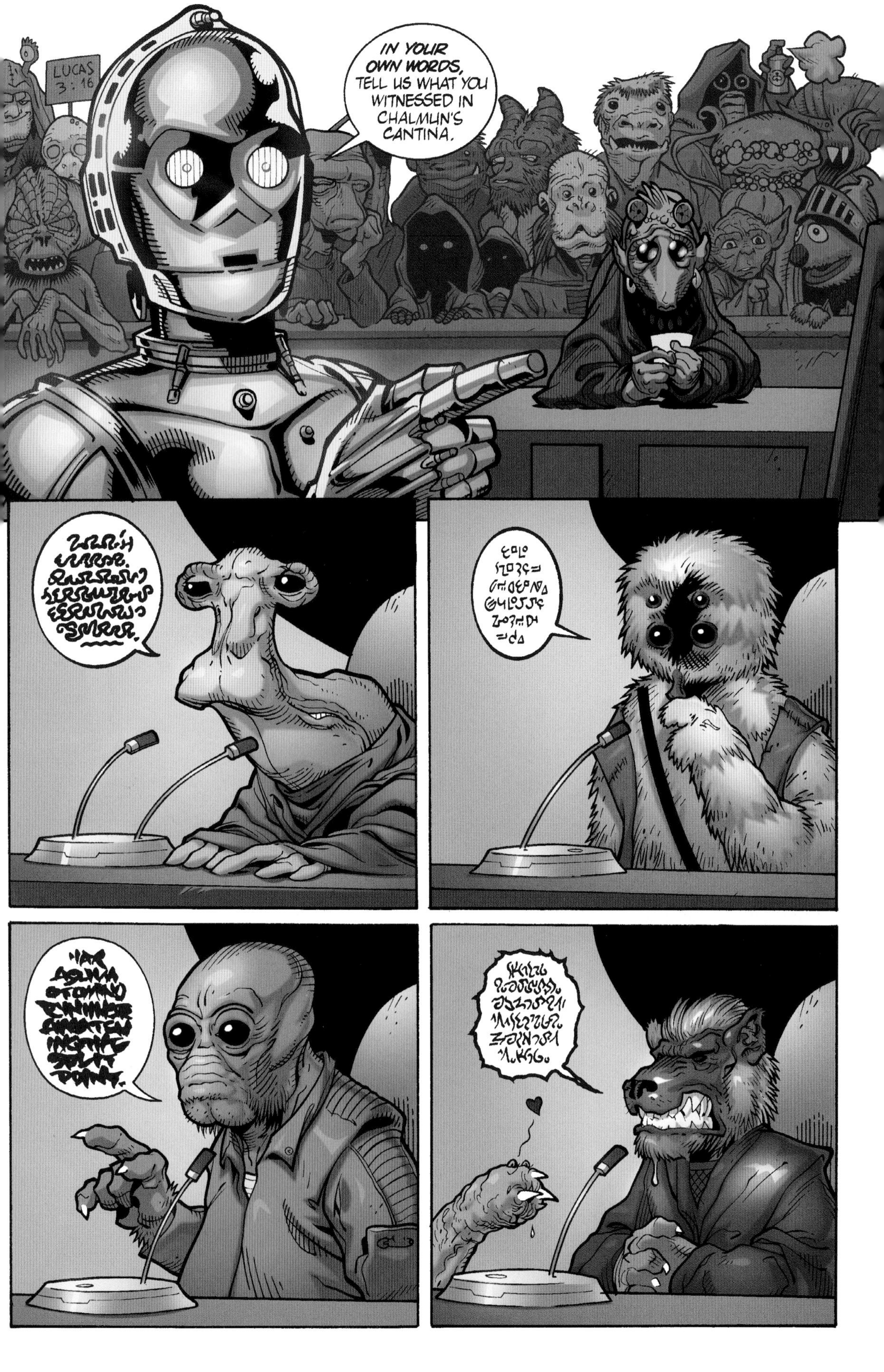

LUCAS 3:16
IN YOUR OWN WORDS, TELL US WHAT YOU WITNESSED IN CHALMUN'S CANTINA.

WE REST OUR CASE, YOUR HONOR.
I OBJECT!
I MEAN, COME ON! THAT WOLF-GUY WASN'T EVEN THERE!
YOUR OBJECTION IS UN-NECESSARY.
THE COURT DOES NOT RECOGNIZE THE TESTIMONY OF VILE ALIEN SPECIES. THEIR STATEMENTS WILL BE STRICKEN FROM THE RECORD.
BESIDES, I CAN'T UNDERSTAND A WORD THEY'RE SAYING.
HOWEVER, CAPTAIN SOLO... IT IS A WELL-KNOWN FACT TO THIS COURT THAT YOU ARE INDEED A SMUGGLER.

AND WHAT DO WE THINK OF *THAT*, LORD VADER?
NOT EXACTLY THE TYPE YOU'D LET DATE YOUR DAUGHTER, MY MASTER.

HA HA HA
YOUR HONOR, NOT ONLY DID GREEDO THREATEN MY LIFE...
...BUT I HAVE ***HOLO EVIDENCE*** THAT'S GOING TO BREAK THIS CASE WIDE OPEN!

...***IRREFUTABLE PROOF*** THAT GREEDO FIRED AT ME ***FIRST!***
WRRR

AS YOU CAN CLEARLY SEE, GREEDO FIRES HIS BLASTER ***BEFORE*** I RETURN FIRE IN ***SELF-DEFENSE!***
WATCH AS AS MY HEAD SKILLFULLY DODGES HIS SHOT, MOVING ***BACK*** AND ***TO THE RIGHT.***

BACK AND TO THE RIGHT...

BACK AND TO THE RIGHT...

BACK AND TO THE RIGHT...

AND THAT'S WHAT *REALLY* HAPPENED!
AT LEAST, *NOW* IT IS...
*OBJECTION, YOUR HONOR!*

THAT HOLO HAS BEEN *ALTERED!*
AND QUITE OBVIOUSLY, MIGHT I ADD...
*ENOUGH!*

LOOK, I'VE GOT AN EMPIRE TO RUN AND FREEDOMS TO DESTROY...
I'LL TAKE A SHORT RECESS AND BE BACK WITH MY VERDICT.
WHO'S GOT A DATE WITH THE DARK SIDE? EMPEROR PALPATINE'S RULING, RIGHT AFTER THIS MESSAGE FROM OUR SPONSOR.

NOW BACK TO "THE EMPEROR'S COURT" AND PALPATINE'S RULING.
CAPTAIN SOLO, I'VE GOT A BAD FEELING ABOUT THIS.
YOU EXPECT THIS COURT TO BELIEVE THAT THE RODIAN FIRED UPON YOU FROM A MERE METER AWAY AND SOMEHOW MANAGED TO MISS?
WHAT WAS HE, A STORM-TROOPER?
HOWEVER, I FEEL IT IS COMPLETELY WITHIN THE NEFARIOUS CHARACTER OF A SMUGGLER, SUCH AS YOURSELF, TO TALK WITH YOUR TRIGGER FINGER.
WHAT KIND OF SPACE PIRATE WOULD WAIT FOR A BOUNTY HUNTER, WHOSE WEAPON IS DRAWN AND IS THREATENING TO KILL YOU, TO FIRE FIRST?
AND YOU HAVE THE AUDACITY TO COME INTO MY COURTROOM AND TRY TO PULL SOME SHENANIGANS WITH THIS BLATANTLY DOCTORED EVIDENCE.
WHAT KIND OF FOOL DO YOU TAKE THIS COURT FOR?
NO ONE SHOULD HAVE THE POWER TO REWRITE HISTORY!
WELL... EXCEPT ME, THAT IS...

AS YOU CAN SEE, MY YOUNG DEFENDANT, YOUR TESTIMONY HAS FAILED.
NOW WITNESS THE JUDICIARY POWER OF THIS *FULLY-ARMED AND OPERATIONAL COURT SYSTEM!*
*SENTENCE AT WILL, LORD VADER!*

THIS COURT FINDS YOU *GUILTY* AND SENTENCES YOU TO LIFE IMPRISONMENT, *FROZEN IN CARBONITE!*

*COURT DISMISSED!*
"SO, CAPTAIN SOLO, WHAT DID YOU THINK OF THE VERDICT?"

WELL, CHEWIE AND I HAVE PULLED SOME CRAZY CONS, BUT EVEN I CAN'T BELIEVE I TRIED TO GET AWAY WITH THAT WHOLE "GREEDO FIRING FIRST" THING.
YES, WELL, GO ON BACK. BOBA FETT IS WAITING FOR YOU.
NEELA, JUSTICE FOR YOUR SON HAS WON OUT THIS DAY. HOW DO YOU FEEL?

I COULDN'T HAVE SAID IT BETTER MYSELF. AND THAT ENDS THIS SESSION OF "THE EMPEROR'S COURT." TUNE IN FOR NEXT WEEK'S TRIAL: MIDI-CHLORIANS VS. THE DIVINE FORCE-- WHAT SHOULD BE TAUGHT IN SCHOOLS?
THIS IS LU-L-N SAYING GOOD NIGHT.

END

<SCAT! GET OUT OF HERE!>
<BAH! USELESS URCHINS!>
YAHHH!
YOW!
URCHINS
WHY DID YOU CHASE THEM OFF? THEY WEREN'T HURTING ANYTHING!
<GET BACK TO WORK, BOY!>
<I'M OFF TO SEE JABBA THE HUTT!>
<IT'S IMPORTANT I SEE HIM BEFORE THE PODRACES THIS AFTERNOON.>

IS WATTO GONE, ANNIE?
YEAH, COME ON IN, GUYS.

WHAT'S IN THIS BOX?
I DON'T KNOW, WALD. WATTO BOUGHT IT FROM SOME PEDDLER.

IT'S A **LIGHT-SABER**!
REALLY? **WOW!**
LET ME SEE THAT!

NO. I FOUND IT FIRST. IT'S MINE!
ACTUALLY, IT'S WATTO'S.

IT DOESN'T WORK. THE POWER MUST BE DEPLETED.
KLK! KLK!
THEY ONLY WORK FOR JEDI KNIGHTS. EVERYONE KNOWS THAT!

SEBULBA HAS FINALLY ARRIVED--WITH HIS NEW PODRACER!
LET'S GO AND SEE IT!

LOOK AT THAT!
WOW!

LOOK--HE HAS A NEW VERTIGO INFLUX OVERRIDE!
WOW!

WHERE? LET ME SEE!
HEY!
YOU DON'T HAVE TO SHOVE!
OOPS!

THE SABER FELL ALL THE WAY TO THE BOTTOM!
I CAN GET IT!
YOU'D BETTER HURRY!

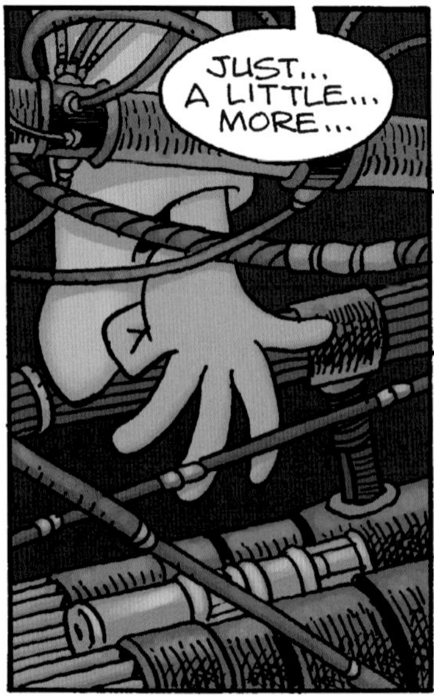
JUST... A LITTLE... MORE...

GOT IT! BUT IT'S **STUCK**!
**HURRY!**
I'M **TRYING!**

<HEY-- GET AWAY FROM THERE!>
UH-OH. HERE COMES SEBULBA!
ALMOST...
HURRY, ANNIE!

UGH!
**THERE!**
FZZZTT
SNAP!

**GOT IT!**
LET'S GET OUT OF HERE!
SPUT!

<...AND STAY AWAY FROM MY RACER!>
YOW!

HUFF HUFF PANT!
HE FINALLY STOPPED CHASING US.
WATTO'S NOT BACK YET. WE'D BETTER PUT THAT LIGHTSABER AWAY.

SOME-DAY I'LL HAVE ONE OF THESE THAT WILL ACTUALLY WORK.
YOU? A JEDI KNIGHT?
HA! HA! HA!

<BAH! JABBA DEMANDS I PAY MY DEBT OR LOSE MY SHOP!>
<THE ONLY WAY I CAN RAISE ENOUGH MONEY IN SO SHORT A TIME IS TO BET ON THE PODRACE-- AGAINST SEBULBA... BUT HE NEVER LOSES!>

<WHAT ARE YOU URCHINS DOING BACK HERE?>
<GET OUT! GET OUT OF MY SHOP! YOU'D BETTER NOT HAVE BEEN TOUCHING MY STUFF!>
UH-OH!

<...AND STAY OUT!>
WAAHHHHHHHHH!

"...AND THEY'RE **OFF**!
"SEBULBA HAS TAKEN AN EARLY LEAD!

"UH-OH. IT LOOKS LIKE ZORCHA IS OUT OF THE RACE!
GOOOMMM!!
"AND SEBULBA IS MAINTAINING HIS LEAD!

YAH HA HA!

HEH. HEH. HEH.

<I'M GOING TO LOSE MY SHOP FOR SURE!>

"IT'S THE FINAL LAP, AND SEBULBA'S LEAD HAS ERODED! IT'S ANYONE'S RACE NOW!
VRRRRR

<GRR... NOW'S THE TIME TO USE THE OVERRIDE!>
CLICK!

FZZZTT!

BOOOM!

"UH-OH. SEBULBA HAS LOST CONTROL OF HIS PODRACER!
WAHH!

EYAHH!
KA-BOOOM!
"IT LOOKS LIKE HE'S OUT OF THE RACE, FOLKS!"

<AH, MY DEBT IS SETTLED, I STILL HAVE MY SHOP, AND I'VE EVEN GOT SOME MONEY LEFT OVER!>
<NOTHING CAN SPOIL MY HAPPY MOOD TODAY!>

<WHAT?! ARE YOU TWO BACK AGAIN?!
UH-OH.
"UH-OH" IS RIGHT.

YOW!
<...AND STAY OUT!>
GANG-WAY!

<FILTHY, WRETCHED URCHINS ... THEY'RE OF NO USE TO ANYONE!>

THE END

MONTHS AFTER THE BATTLE OF GEONOSIS, THE REPUBLIC CLONE TROOPERS HAVE BEGUN TRAINING ON KAMINO WITH THEIR NEW JEDI GENERALS...
GENERAL SECURA! WHAT HAVE YOU DONE?!

# TIDES OF TERROR

I DON'T KNOW... THEY WERE FINE ONE MINUTE, AND THE NEXT...THEY WERE ALL DEAD!

DON'T BLAME HER, GENERAL FISTO.

THESE SOLDIERS WERE INFECTED WITH A DEADLY NANO-VIRUS THAT APPEARS TO MOVE WITH LIGHTNING SPEED. IT'S QUITE AMAZING!

A NANO-VIRUS? ARE WE IN ANY DANGER?

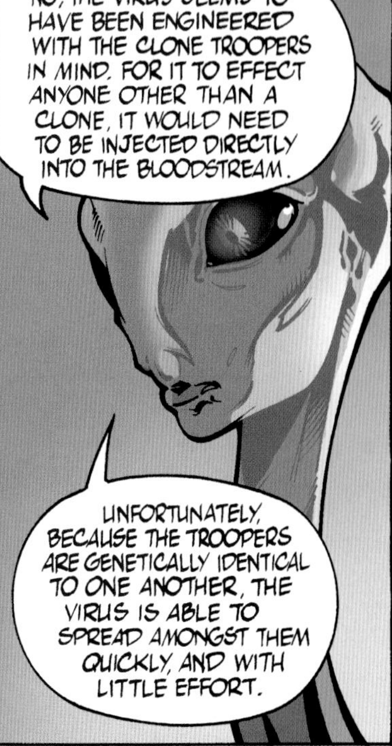

NO, THE VIRUS SEEMS TO HAVE BEEN ENGINEERED WITH THE CLONE TROOPERS IN MIND. FOR IT TO EFFECT ANYONE OTHER THAN A CLONE, IT WOULD NEED TO BE INJECTED DIRECTLY INTO THE BLOODSTREAM.
UNFORTUNATELY, BECAUSE THE TROOPERS ARE GENETICALLY IDENTICAL TO ONE ANOTHER, THE VIRUS IS ABLE TO SPREAD AMONGST THEM QUICKLY, AND WITH LITTLE EFFORT.

NANO-VIRUS TECHNOLOGY IS VERY NEW. UNTIL RECENTLY, IT WAS STRICTLY THEORETICAL. WHOEVER DID THIS WAS EXTREMELY SKILLED.
WHO WOULD BE CAPABLE OF DOING SUCH A THING?
I WOULD SUGGEST SPEAKING WITH THE MASTER CLONER, SAYN TA. TAKE HER THE DATA I'VE COLLECTED SO FAR. SHE SHOULD BE ABLE TO HELP YOU.
LET HER KNOW WE'RE ON OUR WAY. AND LOCK DOWN THIS ENTIRE FACILITY. WE NEED TO QUARANTINE THE TROOPS SO THE VIRUS DOESN'T SPREAD.
THIS IS A DISASTER, KIT!
THAT'S PUTTING IT LIGHTLY, AAYLA. IF WE DON'T STOP THIS HERE AND NOW, THE REPUBLIC WILL BE DEFENSELESS AGAINST THE SEPARATISTS!

SOON, IN THE CENTRAL CLONING LAB...
GENERAL FISTO, GENERAL SECURA! I CAN'T BELIEVE IT! THIS MUST BE A NIGHTMARE!

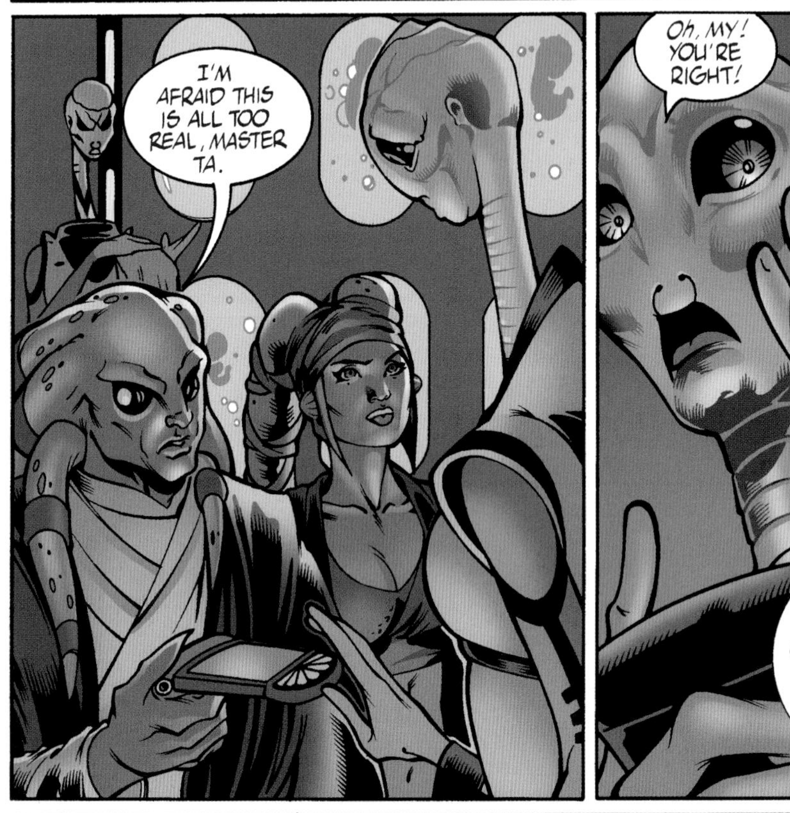
I'M AFRAID THIS IS ALL TOO REAL, MASTER TA.

Oh, MY! YOU'RE RIGHT!
BUT WITH THIS DATA I SHOULD BE ABLE TO SYNTHESIZE A PURE STRAIN OF THE VIRUS.
ONCE I HAVE THAT, CREATING A VACCINE WILL BE SIMPLE.

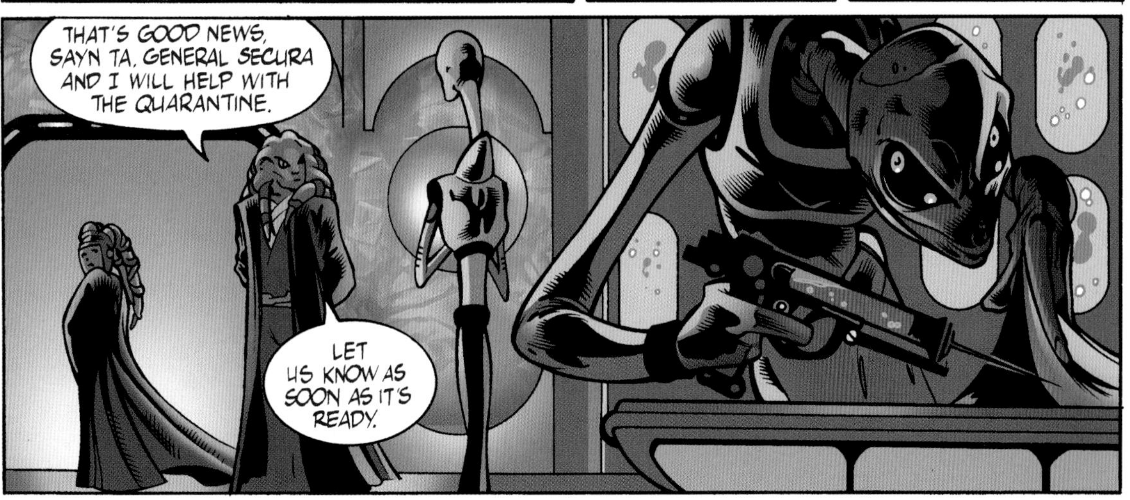
THAT'S GOOD NEWS, SAYN TA. GENERAL SECURA AND I WILL HELP WITH THE QUARANTINE.
LET US KNOW AS SOON AS IT'S READY.

I CAN'T BELIEVE THE SEPARATISTS HAVE SOMEONE WORKING FOR THEM HERE OF ALL PLACES!

THE KAMINOANS ONLY CREATED THE CLONE ARMY FOR THE REPUBLIC BECAUSE THEY WERE PAID TO.

IT ONLY MAKES SENSE THAT THE SEPARATISTS COULD BUY SOMEONE HERE AS WELL...

EEIAAAH!

WHAT HAPPENED?

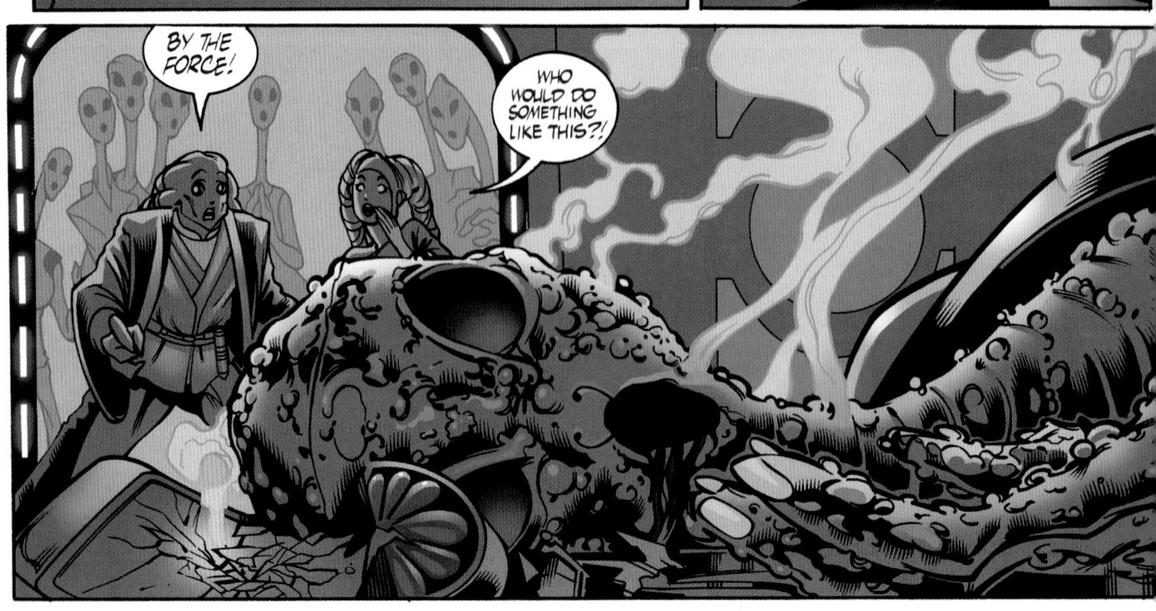
BY THE FORCE!
WHO WOULD DO SOMETHING LIKE THIS?!

"I THINK I HAVE AN IDEA WHO, AAYLA..."

FOLLOW ME...

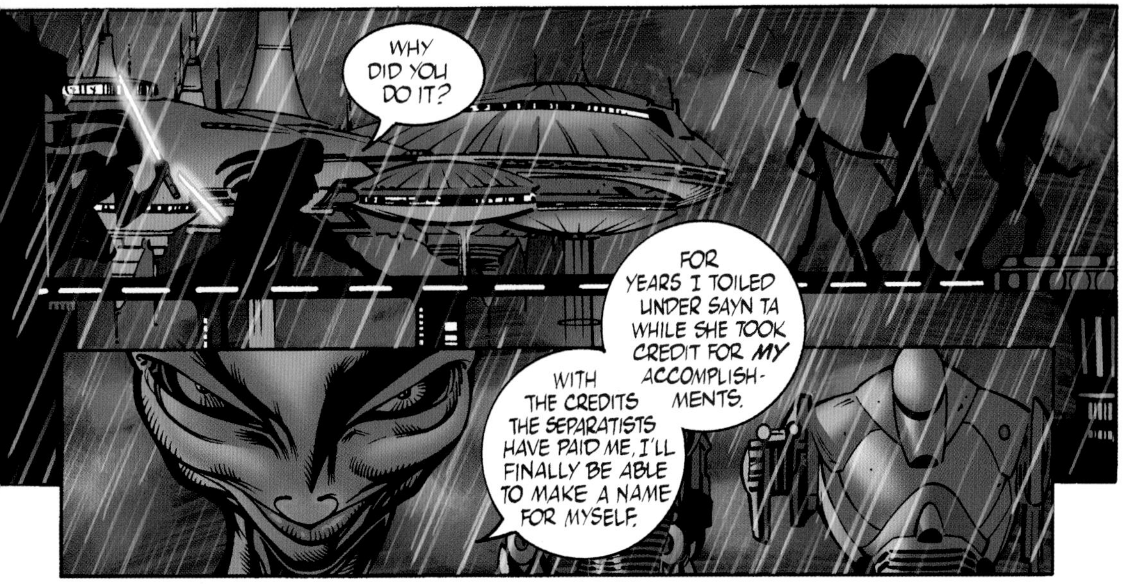
WHY DID YOU DO IT?
FOR YEARS I TOILED UNDER SAYN TA WHILE SHE TOOK CREDIT FOR *MY* ACCOMPLISH-MENTS.
WITH THE CREDITS THE SEPARATISTS HAVE PAID ME, I'LL FINALLY BE ABLE TO MAKE A NAME FOR MYSELF.

ZOW
DESTROY THEM!
ZOW
ZOW
ZOW
ZOW
KZZT
KZZT
ZOW
ZOW

KZZAK

BOOM

BADOOM

KIT!
PLOOSH

...LET ME BREATHE FOR YOU.

AAYLA!
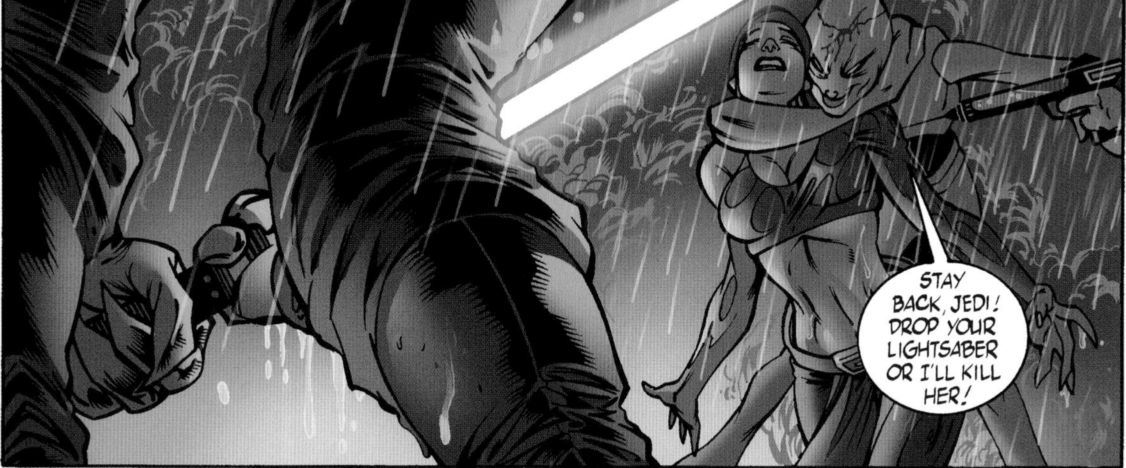
STAY BACK, JEDI! DROP YOUR LIGHTSABER OR I'LL KILL HER!

STUPID JEDI...

FSSS
TCHH

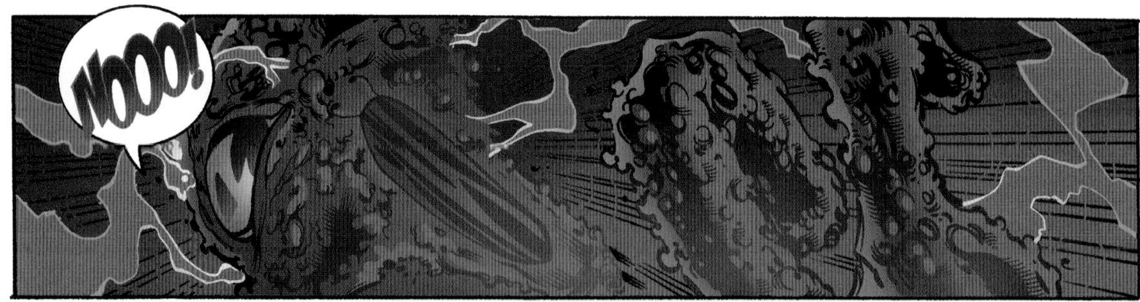
NOOO!

SHE SLIPPED. HOW UNFORTUNATE...
YES, BUT NOW WE HAVE A PURE SAMPLE OF THE VIRUS. CREATING A VACCINE WILL BE SIMPLE.

GENERAL FISTO...I WANT TO THANK YOU FOR SAVING MY LIFE.

IF IT WEREN'T FOR YOU, I WOULD HAVE DROWNED.

ANY TIME, GENERAL SECURA...

...IT WAS MY PLEASURE.

END

THE LESSON
THE BATTLE OF GEONOSIS.

UHN!
ZZZZT

"I DON'T UNDERSTAND, MASTER."

WHAT, DON'T YOU UNDERSTAND, TU'ALA?
THE FORCE FLOWS THROUGH ME, AS IT DOES THROUGH ALL LIVING THINGS, YES, MASTER ZUTH?
THROUGH ALL THINGS, YES.
THEN, AS FAR AS THE FORCE IS CONCERNED, I AM AS IMPORTANT AS ANY OTHER CREATURE.
THEN WHY, unh...
...SHOULD I EVER SACRIFICE MYSELF FOR ANOTHER BEING IF WE ARE EQUALS?
YOU STILL CLING TOO MUCH TO THE FLESH, TU'ALA.
WHAT YOU'RE NOT ACCOUNTING FOR IS DESTINY.
DESTINY?
YES, THAT THE FORCE HAS A PLAN FOR US ALL. FOR ONE, GREATNESS, FOR ANOTHER--
TO DIE A USELESS DEATH?
NOT USELESS, TU'ALA, IF IT AIDS THE FIRST TO ACHIEVE HIS GREATNESS.
I'M SORRY, MASTER ZUTH. IT STILL SEEMS LIKE...

"...TRADING ONE LIFE FOR ANOTHER."
"BE WATCHFUL, TU'ALA."
VMMM
VMMM

I ALWAYS AM, MASTER.
BESIDES, IF THE DANGER OF AN ASSASSINATION ATTEMPT WERE REAL, THE SENATE WOULD HAVE PROVIDED US WITH MORE SECURITY.
YOU BELIEVE SO, DO YOU?

TOOM
OF COURSE.
AARGH!

SNIPER! GET THE AMBASSADOR INSIDE!
WAIT...

FSSSH

MASTER...?

VTT
GAHH!
VTT

*MASTER!* WE NEED TO GET THE DELEGATE AWAY FROM HERE--THERE MAY BE *MORE* ASSASSINS!

MASTER!

SERGEANT! PLEASE GET THE DELEGATE TO HIS QUARTERS.
OF COURSE MISS... MISS, IS THERE ANYTHING...
*NO.* THANK YOU...


"...*I'LL* TEND TO HIM..."

ZZZT

"TU'ALA..."

"BE *STILL,* MASTER."

"YOU *HAVE* TO KNOW, TU'ALA...

"...WHY YOU WOULD SACRIFICE YOURSELF FOR ANOTHER..."
"IT ISN'T THAT THE FORCE LOVES YOU LESS THAN OTHER CREATURES...
AAAAH!
"IT IS THAT YOU LOVE OTHER CREATURES MORE.
"DO YOU UNDERSTAND, TU'ALA?"
I UNDERSTAND, MASTER.
I UNDER-STAND...
END

# SMUGGLER'S BLUES

THE SMUGGLING BUSINESS **SURE** HAS BEEN **SLOW**, CHEWIE. WE HAVEN'T HAD **ONE** JOB SINCE WE HAD TO **DUMP** THAT LAST SHIPMENT OF JABBA'S.

YEOR!

I KNOW, I KNOW -- WE **GOTTA** GET SOME MONEY **FAST** TO PAY BACK JABBA OR WE'RE GONNA WIND UP **BANTHA FODDER**.

YEOAR-YOR ROWR!

WELL **WHY** DIDN'T YOU SAY YOU HAD SOME POTENTIAL **CLIENTS**! WE'LL TALK TO 'EM AND SMOKE OUT THE **HIGHEST** BIDDER.

MAYBE WE'LL GET **LUCKY** AND GET OFFERED **17 THOUSAND**...

YOUR **WOOKIEE** TELLS ME YOUR SHIP IS FOR HIRE -- IS IT **FAST**?

**FAST**?! I'VE MADE THE **KESSEL RUN** IN LESS THAN **12 PARSECS**!

**GOOD!** I'VE GOTTA SHIPMENT OF HOLOGRAPHIC **HUTT-SMUT** THAT ABSOLUTELY, POSITIVELY **MUST** BE DELIVERED OVERNIGHT TO THE **KURLUVION** SYSTEM. THEY JUST **LOVE** HUTT-SMUT THERE, CAN'T GET ENOUGH.

I'D RATHER BE **FROZEN** IN **CARBONITE** AND HUNG UP ON A WALL THAN SMUGGLE THAT **TRASH** -- I'VE GOT **INTEGRITY**, CHUMP.

NEXT UP, **CHEWIE**--

ROOR!
HEY, HEY! STOP SHOVIN'! I'M GOIN' I'M GOIN'!!
HELLO, YOU'RE THE CAPTAIN OF A STARSHIP, RIGHT?
YES I AM. WHAT CAN I DO FOR YOU? YOU NEED TRANSPORT? SOMETHING SHIPPED?
WELL, ACTUALLY, I DON'T NEED TRANSPORT OR ANYTHING LIKE THAT -- I WAS, UH, HOPING YOU MIGHT HAVE A JOB OPENING FOR ME....
Y'KNOW, LIKE A STEWARDESS OR SOMETHING. I COULD HAND OUT PEANUTS. COCKTAILS. CLEAN UP THE SHIP...
LISTEN, WE'RE NOT THAT KIND OF OPERATION, SISTER -- SORRY WE CAN'T HELP YOU.
- SIGH -
I GUESS I'LL JUST HAVE TO TAKE THAT JOB AS A DANCER AT JABBA'S PALACE AFTER ALL....
!
OKAY, CHEWIE -- WHO'S NEXT?
YEWOR.
2.

MR. SOLO, I AM BROTHER XANDO. MY SECT AND I ARE ON A PILGRIMAGE TO NORCLUNE, THE HOLY PLANET. WE SEEK PASSAGE ON YOUR SHIP.
THAT'S QUITE A TRIP -- IT'LL COST YA.
WE OF THE NORCLU ORDER HAVE NO POSSESSIONS...

WE WERE PRAYING THAT YOU WOULD BESTOW THE TRIP AS A GIFT TO THE LIVING FORCE -- ONCE UPON NORCLUNE YOU AND YOUR SHIP SHALL BE BLESSED.
LISTEN, BUDDY -- THE DAY I BELIEVE IN THE "FORCE" IS THE DAY I JOIN THE REBELLION.
NEXT.

WE NEED US TRANSPORT OFFA THIS ROCK -- RIGHT AWAY -- AND WE THINK YOU'LL BE GIVING US A DISCOUNT AS WELL!!
HYUCK.
NOW WHY WOULD I DO THAT?
BECAUSE I HAVE THE DEATH SENTENCE ON 12 SYSTEMS -- ONE MORE WON'T MATTER!
3.

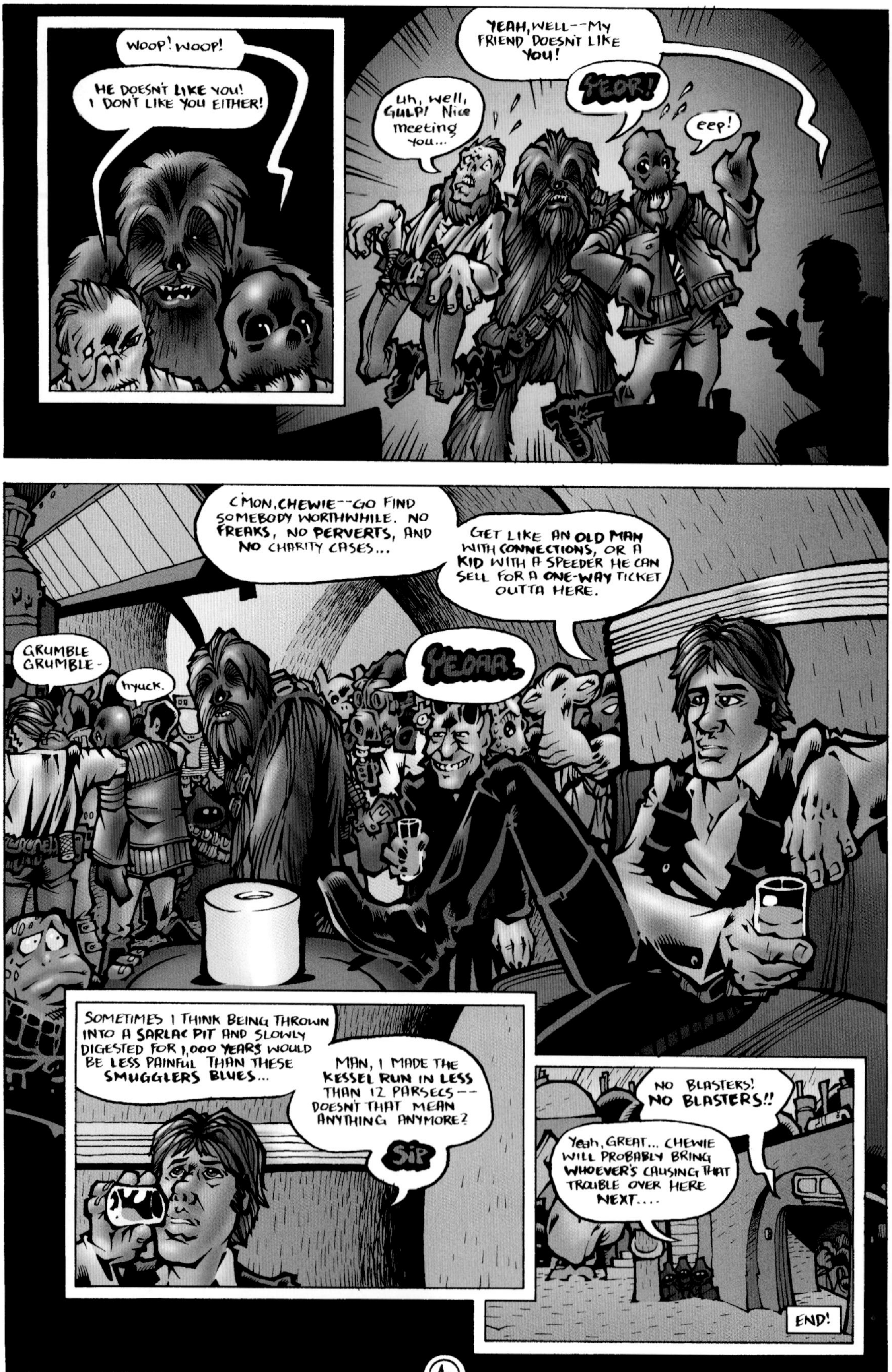

C'MON, CHEWIE--GO FIND SOMEBODY WORTHWHILE. NO FREAKS, NO PERVERTS, AND NO CHARITY CASES...

GET LIKE AN OLD MAN WITH CONNECTIONS, OR A KID WITH A SPEEDER HE CAN SELL FOR A ONE-WAY TICKET OUTTA HERE.

GRUMBLE GRUMBLE-

hyuck.

YEOAR.

SOMETIMES I THINK BEING THROWN INTO A SARLAC PIT AND SLOWLY DIGESTED FOR 1,000 YEARS WOULD BE LESS PAINFUL THAN THESE SMUGGLERS BLUES...

MAN, I MADE THE KESSEL RUN IN LESS THAN 12 PARSECS--DOESN'T THAT MEAN ANYTHING ANYMORE?

SIP

NO BLASTERS! NO BLASTERS!!

Yeah, GREAT... CHEWIE WILL PROBABLY BRING WHOEVER'S CAUSING THAT TROUBLE OVER HERE NEXT....

END!

4.

A LONG TIME AGO, IN A GALAXY FAR, FAR AWAY...

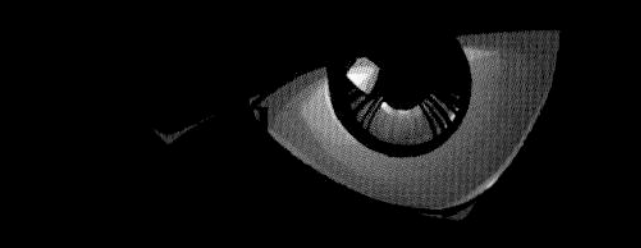

I SENSE FEAR IN YOU.


# MYTHOLOGY

WHAT IS IT YOU FEAR?

DISAPPOINTING YOU...
...MASTER.

OBI-WAN, A JEDI SHALL NOT KNOW ANGER...
...OR FEAR...
...OR HATRED...
...OR LOVE.

LOVE?!
LET GO OF YOUR FEELINGS, OR THEY WILL BE YOUR UNDOING.

FORGIVE ME, MASTER, BUT THERE HAS TO BE A REASON WHY.


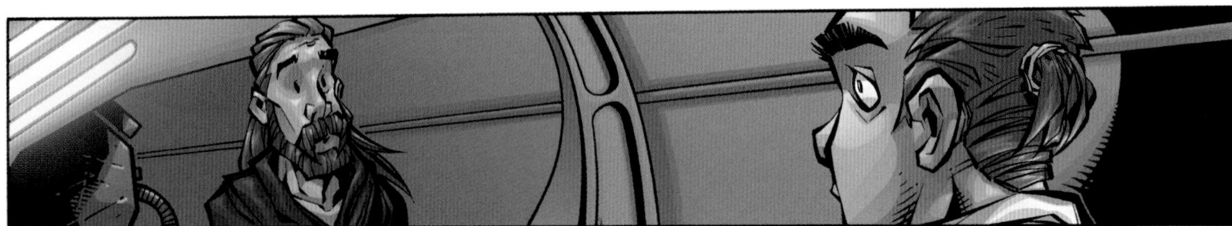

I'M SORRY, MASTER. I DIDN'T MEAN TO--

NO APOLOGIES.
CLEAR YOUR THOUGHTS, YOUNG ONE--

--AND LISTEN TO A STORY.

CALL IT A FABLE.

A PARABLE.

A MYTH, IF YOU WISH.

THOUGH SOME CLAIM IT MAY BE A TRUE STORY WHOSE ORIGINS LIE BURIED IN THE PAST.

WHATEVER IT MAY OR MAY NOT BE, IT IS RELEVANT TO THE JEDI CODE.

"MANY CENTURIES AGO, WHEN THE JEDI ORDER WAS IN ITS *INFANCY,* JEDI MASTERS COMBED THE GALAXY FOR OTHER ***FORCE-SENSITIVE*** BEINGS.

FORGIVE MY INTRUSION, BUT I SEEK THE TWO VOICES THAT CALLED TO ME.

"THIS IS THE TALE OF ***ONE*** SUCH DISCOVERY, AND IT BEGINS WITH THE MASTER ***SHANG-TROY THANABO*** AND ***HIS*** QUEST.

THE ONES ABLE TO CALL ME FROM SUCH A GREAT DISTANCE?

"HE HAD BEEN SEARCHING THE GALAXY FOR SOME TIME AND HAD NOT DISCOVERED ANY LIKE BEINGS. HE SEARCHED WITH HIS ***EYES, EARS*** AND ALSO REACHED OUT WITH THE ***FORCE*** TO NO AVAIL.

"THAT IS, UNTIL HE FELT A ***DISTURBANCE.*** IT WAS LIKE ***NOTHING*** HE EVER FELT BEFORE.

"IT WAS TWO BEINGS, YET ONE, THAT CALLED TO HIM FROM A REMOTE PLANET NAMED ***BORANALL.***

"HE INVESTIGATED.

"HE SEARCHED THE PEOPLE TO FIND THE ***SOURCE*** OF THE DISTURBANCE."

NO. THE TWO THAT CALLED ME ARE IN YOUR BELLY.

"HE WAS ***SURPRISED*** BY HIS DISCOVERY."

"THE TIME CAME FOR THE WOMAN TO GIVE BIRTH.
"THE JEDI MASTER USED THE FORCE TO CALM THE MOTHER AND GUIDE THE CHILDREN.
"ALL WAS GOING WELL UNTIL--
NO!
"AS ONE CHILD WAS COMING OUT, THE OTHER GRABBED ON AS IF NOT WANTING TO BE LEFT ALONE.
"THE MASTER CALMED THE SECOND CHILD AND IT RELEASED HIS BROTHER.
"BUT THERE WOULD ALWAYS BE A SCAR.
"SHANG-TROY EXPLAINED THAT THE FORCE WAS STRONG IN THE TWO BABIES, IT WAS LIKE NOTHING HE'D EVER KNOWN, AND THAT IT WAS HIS DUTY TO RAISE THEM TO BE JEDI KNIGHTS.
"HE WOULD TAKE THEM AND RAISE THEM. THE MOTHER, UNABLE TO PROVIDE FOR THE TWO, AGREED.
"IT WAS DECIDED BY SHANG-TROY THAT HE WOULD TRAIN THE TWO HIMSELF ON A REMOTE PLANET.

"THE TWO BEINGS THAT USED TO BE ONE WERE INFINITELY MORE POWERFUL TOGETHER THAN WHEN SEPARATED-- MORE POWERFUL THAN ANY OTHER JEDI EVER KNOWN.
"SHANG-TROY BEGAN HIS TRAINING. THE BOYS BEGAN LEARNING, AND THE MASTER DISCOVERED THINGS AS WELL.
"THE IDENTICAL TWINS SHARED A SPECIAL BOND, STRONGER THAN ANY JEDI. THEY COULD ANTICIPATE THE OTHER'S MOVEMENTS, READ EACH OTHER'S THOUGHTS, BUT THERE WAS ONE THING THAT WAS MORE STARTLING--A UNIQUE GIFT THE TWO SHARED.
"THEY ALSO EQUALED EACH OTHERS' SKILL IN THE FORCE, IN FACT WERE VIRTUALLY IDENTICAL, SAVE THE BIRTHMARK ON THE ONE'S ARM.
"AS THEY GREW INTO YOUNG ADULTHOOD, THE BOYS HAD KNOWN ONLY TRAINING AND MEDITATION-- LEARNING NOTHING OF THE OUTSIDE UNIVERSE.
"BUT, THEY HAD GROWN POWERFUL IN THE FORCE AND HAD COME TO LOVE THE OLD MASTER AS A FATHER."
HA! WE DID IT! WE FINALLY BEAT YOU, MASTER!
IT IS TIME.
"IT WAS TIME FOR THE BOYS TO USE ALL THEY HAD LEARNED TO HELP BRING PEACE TO THE GALAXY."

THEY JOURNEYED ALL OVER THE GALAXY FIGHTING THE FORCES OF EVIL, KNOWING ONLY THE STRONG BOND THAT THEY FELT.
"THE KNOWLEDGE THAT THE OTHER WOULD ALWAYS BE THERE--
"--THAT IS, UNTIL THEY MET HER.
"FOR YOU SEE, SHE FELL IN LOVE WITH THE YOUNGER BROTHER, AND THE OLDER SIBLING GREW JEALOUS, FOR BEING IDENTICAL, HE LOVED HER JUST AS MUCH, BUT COULDN'T HAVE HER."

"THE OLD MASTER TRIED TO COMFORT THE BOY, BUT HE WAS ANGRY AND JEALOUS AND IN LOVE. A BAD COMBINATION.

"YET ALL SEEMED TO BE FINE-- UNTIL THAT NIGHT.
"A SURPRISE VISIT.

" YOU MUST REMEMBER THAT THE BOYS WERE VIRTUALLY IDENTICAL EXCEPT FOR ONE THING.

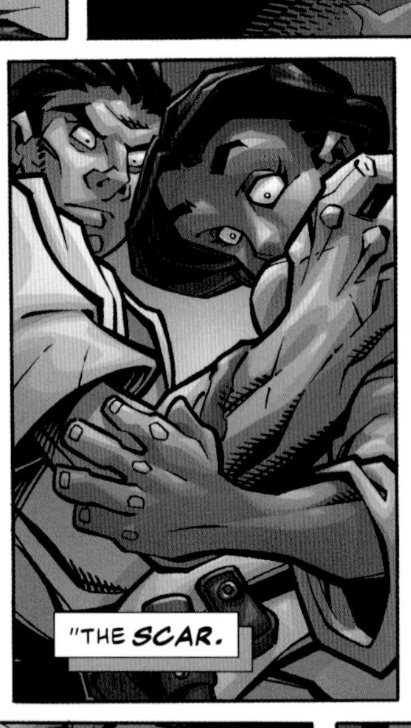
"THE SCAR.

"HE HAD BETRAYED A TRUST. A TRUST NOT EASILY GAINED. BUT THE TWO HAD A LINK-- HE FORGOT THAT HIS BROTHER KNEW WHAT HE MIGHT DO, THE MINUTE HE THOUGHT OF IT.

"HE HOPED HIS BROTHER WOULD HAVE SHOWN RESTRAINT-- BUT THE INTENSE JEALOUSY BURNED IN HIS SOUL--IN BOTH OF THEM NOW.

"THEIR WORDS SOON BECAME HEATED...
"...FILLED WITH ANGER AND FEAR.
"THEIR MASTER, SENSING THE DISTURBANCE, RAN TO THE SCENE IN HOPES OF CALMING HIS ACOLYTES.
"HE REACHED OUT WITH THE FORCE, BUT TO NO EFFECT. THEY WERE BEYOND RATIONAL THOUGHT--THEIR EMOTIONS WERE TOO STRONG.
"THEY CONTINUED TO GROW MORE VIOLENT, MORE WILD, MORE INTENSE UNTIL...
"...THERE WAS NO TURNING BACK.
"THEIR LOVE, JEALOUSY, FEAR AND ANGER WAS DIRECTED SOLELY AT THE OTHER BROTHER, BUT AS WITH MOST ARGUMENTS, THE ONES YOU HURT MOST..."

"THEIR RAGE OVERTOOK THEM... THE FIGHTING TURNED DEADLY. THEY HAD KILLED THE ONE PERSON WHO MEANT MORE TO THEM, THAT CARED FOR THEM MORE THAN ANYONE IN THE GALAXY.
"...ARE THE INNOCENT PEOPLE YOU LOVE.
"AND EACH BLAMED THE OTHER.
"THE INTENSITY AND VITRIOL OF THE BATTLE BEGAN TURNING WHITE-HOT.
"THE GIRL BEGGED THEM TO STOP, NOT TO MAKE IT ANY WORSE...
"BUT THEIR ANGER WAS SO DEEP, IT MADE THEM UNABLE TO EVEN HEAR HER. TO THEM, HER MOUTH WAS MOVING, BUT NO WORDS WERE COMING OUT.
"SHE PLEADED, SCREAMED, DID ALL SHE COULD UNTIL THERE WAS NOTHING LEFT FOR HER TO DO.
"NOTHING, SAVE RUN AWAY."

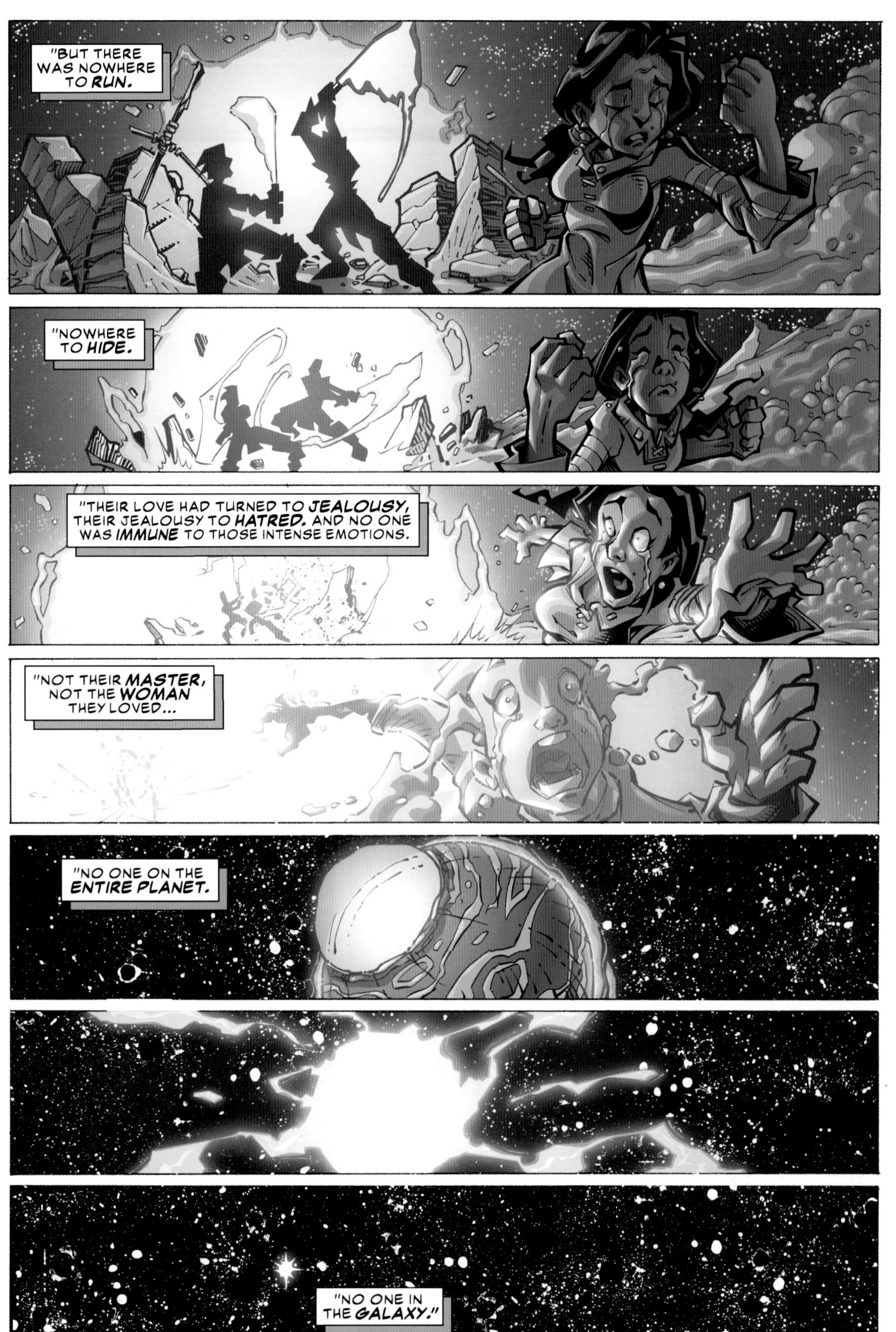
"BUT THERE WAS NOWHERE TO RUN.
"NOWHERE TO HIDE.
"THEIR LOVE HAD TURNED TO JEALOUSY, THEIR JEALOUSY TO HATRED. AND NO ONE WAS IMMUNE TO THOSE INTENSE EMOTIONS.
"NOT THEIR MASTER, NOT THE WOMAN THEY LOVED...
"NO ONE ON THE ENTIRE PLANET.
"NO ONE IN THE GALAXY."

YOU SEE, OBI-WAN, THEIR INTENSE EMOTIONS OVERTOOK THEM, AND THAT STAR WILL ALWAYS REMIND US OF THAT.

THE TWO WHO WERE ONE WERE NOW ONE AGAIN. THEY WERE EQUAL IN EVERY WAY, AND NEITHER COULD GET THE BETTER OF THE OTHER.
A STALEMATE. A STALEMATE WITH NO ENDING.

SOME SAY THAT THEY BATTLE TO THIS DAY-- THEIR ANGER FUELING THE FIRE OF THAT STAR.

MANY IN THE ORDER STILL BELIEVE THAT IS WHY A MASTER MAY ONLY HAVE ONE PADAWAN, AND THAT INTENSE FEELINGS OF BOTH ANGER AND LOVE ARE FORBIDDEN.

PASSION CLOUDS AN OTHERWISE BALANCED MIND, AND IT SHOULD BE AVOIDED. THAT IS ONE LESSON A MASTER MUST ALWAYS IMPART.

ONE DAY YOU WILL BECOME A MASTER, AND THE TIME WILL COME FOR YOU TO INSTRUCT ANOTHER.

WHEN THAT TIME COMES, BE MINDFUL OF THIS LESSON AND REMEMBER OUR CODE; A JEDI SHALL NOT KNOW FEAR, OR HATRED OR ANGER... OR LOVE, FOR IT WILL CONSUME YOU AND LEAD TO THE DARK SIDE.

REMEMBER THAT, OBI-WAN.
I WILL, MASTER.
END.

LARS HOMESTEAD-- TATOOINE
I THINK YOU MIGHT HAVE BEEN A LITTLE TOO ROUGH ON LUKE, OWEN. IT'S ONLY NATURAL THAT THE BOY WOULD WANT TO KNOW ABOUT HIS FATHER AND--
THERE'S TOO MUCH WORK TO DO IN THE PRESENT TO BE WASTING TIME DAYDREAMING ABOUT THE PAST--
Sandstorm

--AND I DIDN'T PUNISH HIM FOR ASKING, I PUNISHED HIM FOR LOSING HIS TEMPER WHEN HE DIDN'T GET WHAT HE WANTED.

:sigh: WELL, ANAKIN WASN'T ANY DIFFERENT...

THAT'S EXACTLY THE POINT. LUKE IS GOING TO BE DIFFERENT.

THEN PERHAPS YOU SHOULD HAVE CHANGED HIS NAME FROM SKYWALKER ALTOGETHER!

BUT THAT WOULDN'T BE VERY FAIR TO THE MEMORY OF SHMI, WOULD IT?

"A COUPLE OF DAYS RESTRICTED TO THE FARM ISN'T GOING TO KILL HIM, BERU.

"BESIDES, HE WOULDN'T HAVE BEEN ABLE TO GO INTO ANCHORHEAD WITH HIS FRIENDS WITH THIS SANDSTORM KICKING UP--

"--ANYONE CAUGHT OUT IN A STORM LIKE THIS WILL FIND THEMSELVES BURIED IN THEIR GRAVE--

"I JUST WISH THE STORM COULD BURY THE PAST THE SAME WAY."

:cough:
:cough:
:cough:
--have a twin sister. Your feelings have now betrayed her.

Come with me. It is the only way.
IS SOMEBODY THERE...?

The Force is strong with this one...

ARE YOU OKAY?

YOU DON'T LOOK TOO WELL...
I'LL BE ALL RIGHT...
*cough-cough* I THOUGHT YOU MIGHT HAVE BEEN A TUSKEN RAIDER OR SOMETHING...

NO--NOTHING THAT SINISTER.
MY NAME'S ANNIE--

--AND I THINK I'M LOST.
HI, ANNIE. WELCOME TO THE CLUB. I'M LUKE--BUT EVERYONE CALLS ME "WORMIE" BECAUSE I'M THE LITTLE GUY--
--UNFORTUNATELY...

THEN I'LL CALL YOU LUKE--

--I KNOW ALL ABOUT WHAT IT'S LIKE TO BE THE "LITTLE GUY."

--AND SO I FINALLY DECIDED TO JUST RUN AWAY.
I'M SO TIRED OF GETTING INTO TROUBLE FOR ASKING ABOUT MY FATHER. IT'S NOT FAIR!
ALL I KNOW IS THAT HE WAS A NAVIGATOR ON A SPICE FREIGHTER-- AND THAT HE'S DEAD NOW...

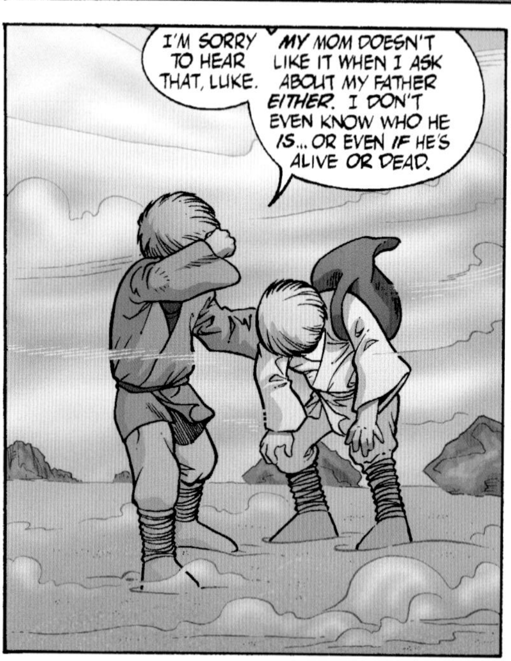
I'M SORRY TO HEAR THAT, LUKE.
MY MOM DOESN'T LIKE IT WHEN I ASK ABOUT MY FATHER EITHER. I DON'T EVEN KNOW WHO HE IS... OR EVEN IF HE'S ALIVE OR DEAD.

IT'S JUST MY MOM AND ME, SO IT GETS A LITTLE LONELY SOMETIMES.
YOU DON'T HAVE ANY BROTHERS OR SISTERS?
NOPE--BUT SOMETIMES I WISH I DID. YOU'RE LUCKY YOU'VE EVEN GOT A MOM.

I'VE GOT A FEW FRIENDS, BUT IT'S NOT THE SAME THING.
PLUS, I'M NOT ALLOWED OFF THE MOISTURE FARM VERY MUCH...
...AUNT BERU SAYS I'M PRONE TO DUST FEVER...

I'D SAY YOU WERE A BIT MORE THAN PRONE TO IT--YOU'RE LOOKING LIKE SOMETHING THE SCURRIER DRAGGED IN. MAYBE WE SHOULD--

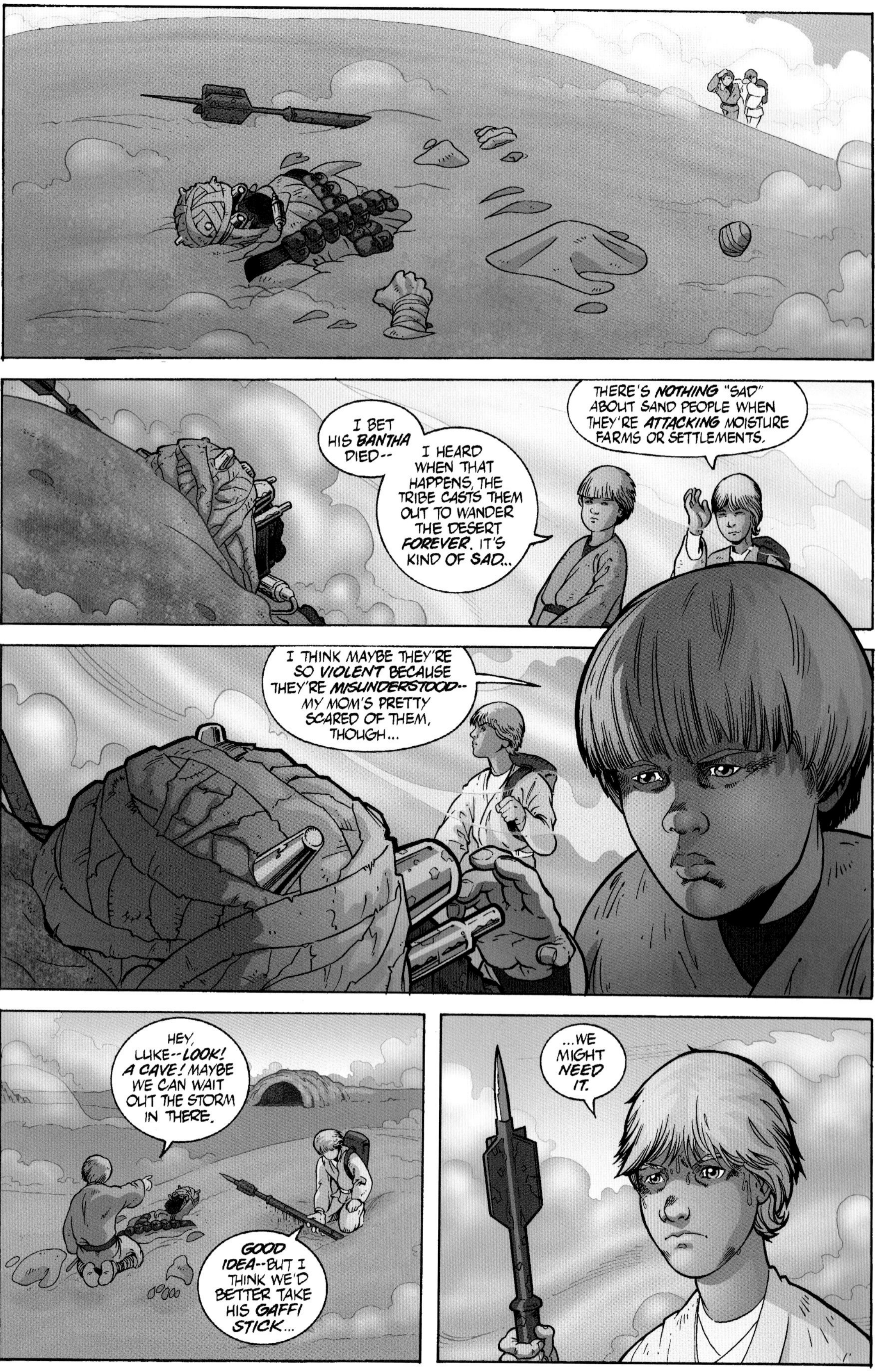

I BET HIS *BANTHA* DIED--
I HEARD WHEN THAT HAPPENS, THE TRIBE CASTS THEM OUT TO WANDER THE DESERT *FOREVER*. IT'S KIND OF *SAD*...
THERE'S *NOTHING* "SAD" ABOUT SAND PEOPLE WHEN THEY'RE *ATTACKING* MOISTURE FARMS OR SETTLEMENTS.
I THINK MAYBE THEY'RE SO *VIOLENT* BECAUSE THEY'RE *MISUNDERSTOOD*-- MY MOM'S PRETTY SCARED OF THEM, THOUGH...

HEY, LUKE--*LOOK! A CAVE!* MAYBE WE CAN WAIT OUT THE STORM IN THERE.
*GOOD IDEA*--BUT I THINK WE'D BETTER TAKE HIS *GAFFI STICK*...

...WE MIGHT *NEED IT*.

SON OF A NERFHERDER! I LOST MY HAT!
I LOVED THAT HAT...
LOOK AT THIS STORM! WHY WOULD ANYONE WANT TO LIVE ON THIS DIRT-BALL OF A PLANET?
ONE DAY-- NO MATTER WHAT IT TAKES...

...I'M GONNA LEAVE TATOOINE, BECOME A PILOT, AND LIVE A LIFE OF ADVENTURE!
HEY, THAT'S MY DREAM, TOO! I WANT TO BE A PILOT SO BAD. WHAT I REALLY WANT IS ONE OF INCOM'S NEW T-16 SKYHOPPERS. SOME OF THE OLDER KIDS HAVE THEM AND THEY FLY THEM THROUGH BEGGAR'S CANYON.
I HAVEN'T HEARD OF THOSE, BUT IT SOUNDS GREAT! YOU KNOW, I'M EVEN THINKING OF BUILDING MY OWN POD-RACER!

WOW! THAT'S--
HEY! WHAT'S A PODRA--

DUCK!

AGGH! THEY MUST HAVE BEEN ATTRACTED TO THE FIRE!

WELL, IF THEY LIKE THE FIRE SO MUCH, THEY CAN HAVE IT!

WATCH OUT!

THERE'S TOO MANY OF THEM!
LET'S GET OUT OF HERE!

HOW DID YOU KNOW THEY WERE GOING TO ATTACK?
I CAN'T REALLY EXPLAIN IT. SOMETIMES I JUST... SENSE THINGS, AND--

ANNIE!
OOF!

IT'S AN ASTROMECH DROID--LOOKS LIKE AN R5 SERIES. I WONDER HOW IT GOT OUT HERE?
SOME JAWAS MUST HAVE LEFT IT BEHIND OR SOMETHING...

I THINK I CAN USE ITS MOTIVATOR TO CREATE AN ENERGY SURGE AND SEND UP A FLARE--BUT IT'LL FRY IN THE PROCESS...
cough cough HOW DO YOU KNOW ALL THAT?
I'M PRETTY GOOD WITH ANY KIND OF MACHINE.
I JUST SEEM TO UNDER-STAND HOW THEY WORK. I'M EVEN BUILDING MY OWN DROID TO HELP OUT AROUND THE HOUSE.

I GUESS I JUST LIKE TO FIX THINGS--MAKE THEM RIGHT. IF I COULD, I'D MAKE EVERYTHING IN THE WHOLE GALAXY THE WAY IT SHOULD BE.
SOMETIMES I FEEL THE SAME WAY...

...BUT THEN, I FIGURE PEOPLE SHOULD BE ALLOWED TO MAKE THEIR OWN CHOICES--THOUGH I SUPPOSE MY CHOICE GOT ME STUCK OUT IN THIS BLASTED STORM...
SEE? PEOPLE USUALLY DON'T KNOW WHAT'S FOR THEIR OWN GOOD.

heh-heh OKAY, THEN--AS LONG AS YOU MAKE IT SO I CAN GET OFF THIS DUSTBOWL, YOU'VE GOT MY VOTE!
HOW DID YOU END UP LOST OUT HERE, ANYWAY?
YOU KNOW... I'M NOT SURE.
VUURR

THAT'S NO SHIP!

ANNIE!
FWOOSH

IF THIS IS A *DREAM*, ANNIE, I WISH WE'D *WAKE UP!*
ROARRR!

ANNIE...?

WHAT DO I DO?
GRARRR

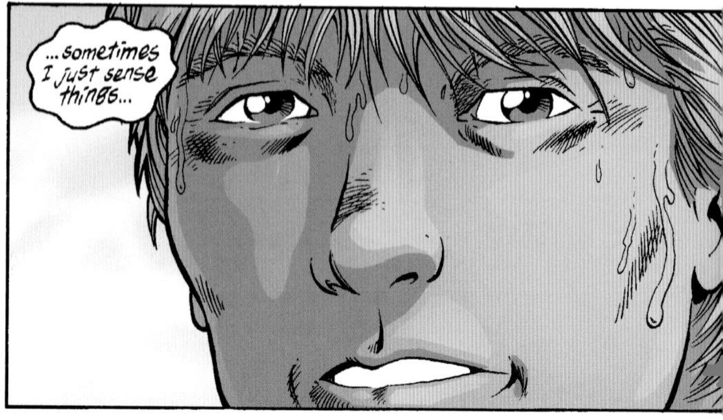
...sometimes I just sense things...

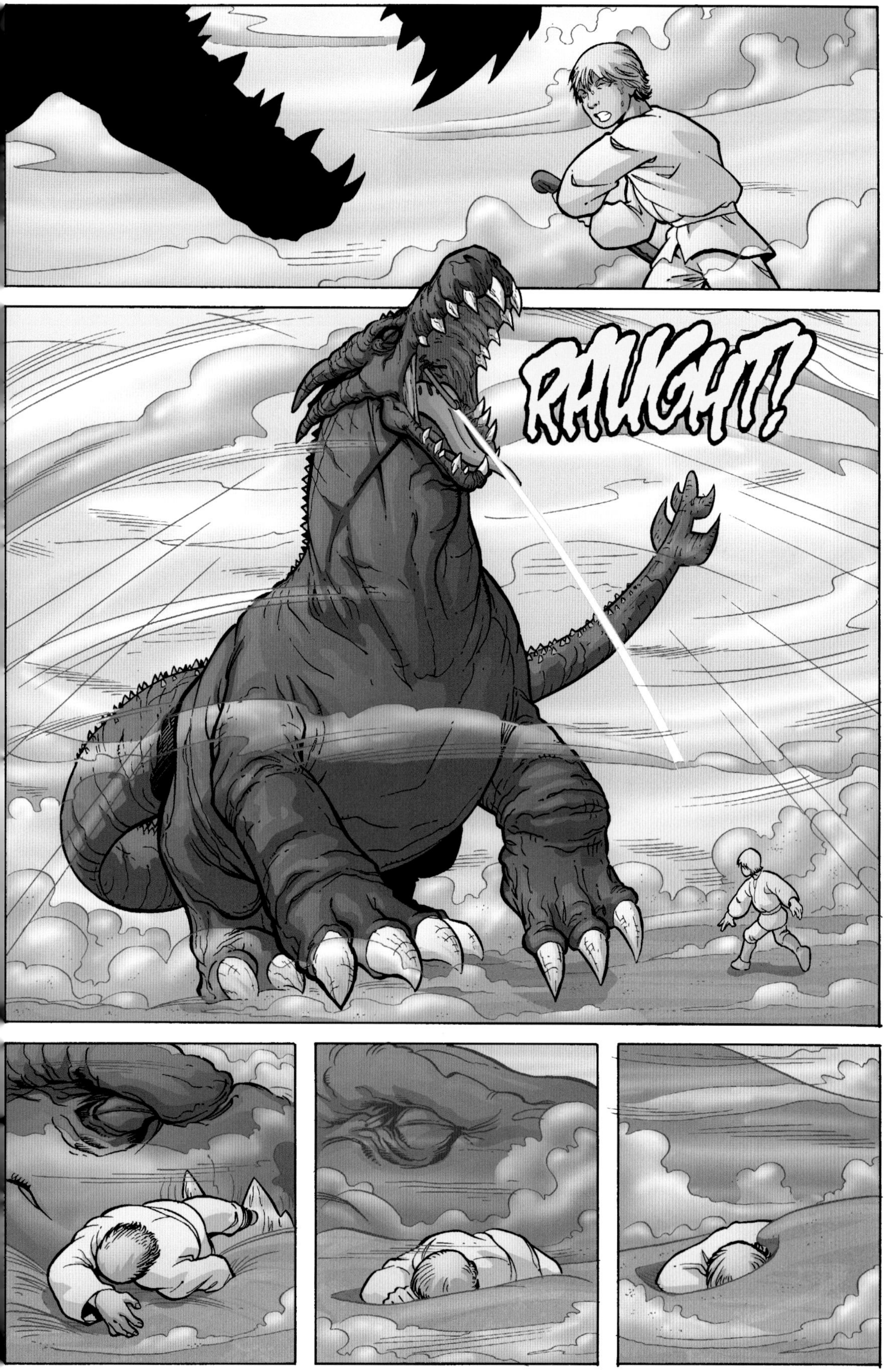

RAUGHT!

LUKE!

Oh, LUKE--
I THOUGHT I'D LOST YOU, BOY...
cough cough cough
UNCLE OWEN? BUT WHERE'S--DID I KILL THE KRAYT DRAGON?

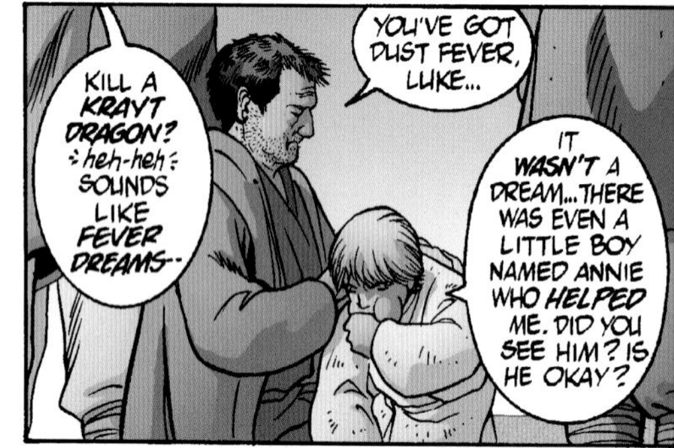
KILL A KRAYT DRAGON? heh-heh SOUNDS LIKE FEVER DREAMS--
YOU'VE GOT DUST FEVER, LUKE...
IT WASN'T A DREAM... THERE WAS EVEN A LITTLE BOY NAMED ANNIE WHO HELPED ME. DID YOU SEE HIM? IS HE OKAY?

--THOUGH HOW A TEN-YEAR-OLD KID MANAGED TO SURVIVE ONE OF TATOOINE'S TOUGHEST SANDWHIRLS IN HISTORY IS BEYOND ME...
ANNIE...

HE'S A SPECIAL BOY.
END

# First Impressions

CORUSCANT, MID-MORNING.

FATHER, *PLEASE* LET ME EXPLORE THE CITY, JUST FOR A LITTLE WHILE. I PROMISE TO BE BACK IN PLENTY OF TIME FOR THE RECEPTION.

LEIA, THIS IS YOUR FIRST TIME ON CORUSCANT. I DON'T WANT YOU GOING OFF ON YOUR OWN.

THIS IS A VERY LARGE AND DANGEROUS CITY. YOU CAN GO EXPLORING, *AS LONG AS* YOU TAKE TWO GUARDS WITH YOU.

BUT FATHER, I WANT TO GO BY MYSEL--

TWO GUARDS OR NO DEAL. TAKE IT OR LEAVE IT, LEIA.

ALL RIGHT, FATHER.
GOOD. NOW GO AHEAD. BUT BE BACK BY THE AFTER-NOON! WE MUST BE AT THE IMPERIAL PALACE BY EARLY EVENING.

I WILL, FATHER, I PROMISE.

LET'S STOP FOR SOMETHING TO EAT. THAT RESTAURANT OVER THERE LOOKS GOOD.
MAYBE WE SHOULD LOOK FOR A PLACE IN A BETTER AREA, YOUR HIGH-NESS.
NONSENSE. THIS IS FINE.
PLEASE, I DO NOT WANT TROUBLE. I MERELY WISH TO PURCHASE A MEAL.
I AM SURE THERE IS NO HARM IN THAT.
LIKE I SAID BEFORE, MOVE ALONG. THIS IS NO PLACE FOR YOU.
YOUR KIND BELONGS ELSEWHERE.
SEE HERE. THERE IS NO NEED FOR FORCE. THIS IS NOT FAIR! ALL I WANT--
ENOUGH!
TUMP
NO!

STOP!
HOW DARE YOU? HE DID NOTHING WRONG! LEAVE HIM ALO--

IMPERIAL BUSINESS. THIS IS NO CONCERN OF YOURS. NOW MOVE ALONG AND LET US DO OUR JOB.
MY FATHER IS IN THE IMPERIAL SENATE! I DOUBT THAT HE WILL TOLERATE--

GET HER OUT OF HERE OR WE'LL THROW HER IN A DETENTION CELL, TOO.
YOUR HIGHNESS, PLEASE, WE MUST GET YOU BACK TO YOUR FATHER.

THIS IS OUTRAGEOUS! MY FATHER WILL PUT A STOP TO THIS, I PROMISE YOU!

IT WAS AWFUL, FATHER. THEY BEAT AND ARRESTED HIM WITH-OUT A SECOND'S HESITATION! I JUST COULDN'T STAND THERE--I HAD TO DO SOMETHING.
I KNOW, LEIA, BUT PUTTING YOUR OWN SAFETY AT RISK IS NOT THE BEST WAY TO RESOLVE A SITUATION! THIS IS THE IMPERIAL CAPITAL! YOU MUST BE CAREFUL HERE. PALPATINE HAS SPIES EVERYWHERE, AND MY DIPLOMATIC IMMUNITY MAY NOT PROTECT YOU IF YOU GO TOO FAR.

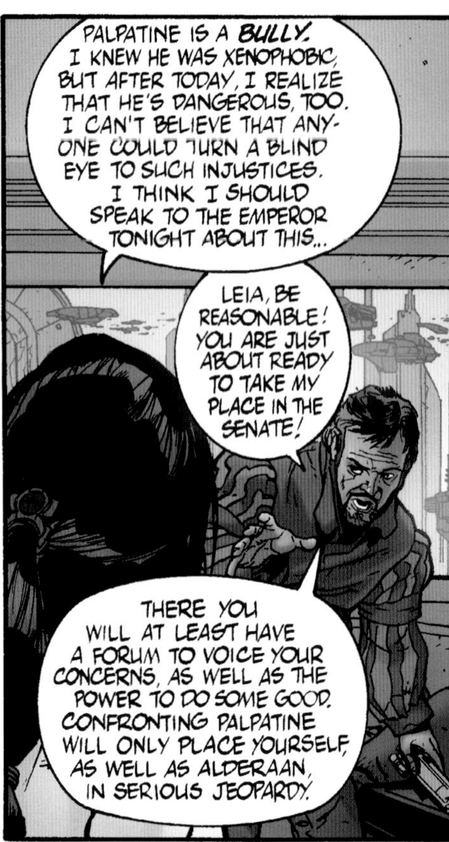
PALPATINE IS A BULLY. I KNEW HE WAS XENOPHOBIC, BUT AFTER TODAY, I REALIZE THAT HE'S DANGEROUS, TOO. I CAN'T BELIEVE THAT ANY-ONE COULD TURN A BLIND EYE TO SUCH INJUSTICES. I THINK I SHOULD SPEAK TO THE EMPEROR TONIGHT ABOUT THIS...
LEIA, BE REASONABLE! YOU ARE JUST ABOUT READY TO TAKE MY PLACE IN THE SENATE!
THERE YOU WILL AT LEAST HAVE A FORUM TO VOICE YOUR CONCERNS, AS WELL AS THE POWER TO DO SOME GOOD. CONFRONTING PALPATINE WILL ONLY PLACE YOURSELF, AS WELL AS ALDERAAN, IN SERIOUS JEOPARDY.

I DON'T WANT TO HIDE JUST BECAUSE SOME DICTATOR HAS AN ARMY OF BRUTES AT HIS BECK AND CALL.
I REFUSE TO BE SILENT, FATHER! I WILL TALK WITH PALPATINE TONIGHT!

LEIA, ENOUGH! YOU HAVE NEVER MET THE EMPEROR BEFORE, AND I CAN ASSURE YOU, HE IS NOT A FLEXIBLE OR REASONABLE MAN!

BUT FATHER...
LEIA, THE MATTER DROPS HERE!
NOW GO AND GET DRESSED OR WE'LL BE LATE!

GRAND RECEPTION HALL, IMPERIAL PALACE.
ALL THIS POMP AND BLATANT VULGARITY, ALL IN THE NAME OF CURRYING FAVOR WITH PALPATINE. IT'S APPALLING.
THE EMPIRE IS MIRED IN BLATANT DISPLAYS OF POWER AND HIERARCHY.
DISPLAYS LIKE THIS ARE DESIGNED TO CLEARLY CEMENT HIS POWER TO THOSE WHO WOULD BE FOOLISH ENOUGH TO HAVE ANY DOUBTS ABOUT WHO THEY SHOULD BE LOYAL TO.

I KNOW WHAT YOU'RE THINKING, LEIA. PLEASE DON'T DO ANYTHING WE'LL REGRET LATER.
I WON'T, FATHER, I PROMISE.

STEADY, LEIA.

SENATOR ORGANA. I SEE YOU HAVE BROUGHT YOUR DAUGHTER WITH YOU.
YOUR HIGHNESS, MAY I PRESENT THE PRINCESS LEIA.

A PLUCKY LITTLE THING, ISN'T SHE? YESSS...

YOU HAVE YOUR FATHER'S FIRE.
I LOOK FORWARD TO SEEING YOUR PRETTY YOUNG FACE IN THE SENATE.
TH-THANK YOU, YOUR HIGHNESS.

EXCELLENT.

ARE YOU ALL RIGHT, LEIA?

HE WAS SO... EVIL, FATHER. AS IF HE WAS PITCH BLACK INSIDE.

I'M SORRY YOU HAD TO FIND OUT THE HARD WAY. CONFRONTING PALPATINE WOULD HAVE BEEN A FUTILE GESTURE, LEIA. HE'S TOO POWERFUL.

HE WOULD HAVE TO BE POWERFUL TO FRIGHTEN SOMEONE AS STRONG AS YOU, LEIA.
I'M READY TO TAKE YOUR PLACE IN THE SENATE, FATHER. I KNOW I CAN MAKE A DIFFERENCE THERE, OR AT LEAST TRY TO.
I WILL MAKE YOU PROUD OF ME.

Oh, LEIA. YOU ALREADY HAVE. THERE ARE MANY WAYS OF MAKING A DIFFERENCE.
MOST ARE MADE QUIETLY, THROUGH MORE...UNDERGROUND MEANS. SOMETIMES DIFFERENCES ARE MADE ONE AT A TIME, AND ARE SO SMALL THEY DO NOT REGISTER WITH EVERYONE, YET CAN HAVE PROFOUND REVERBERATIONS.
WHAT DO YOU MEAN, FATHER?

I MADE SOME INQUIRIES AND TRACKED DOWN THE DETENTION CENTER YOUR CAAMASI FRIEND WAS TAKEN TO. I ARRANGED FOR HIS RELEASE.
YOU CAN GO MAKE SURE IT'S ALL TAKEN CARE OF. SEE THAT HE'S RELEASED AND MAKES IT HOME SAFELY. TAKE YOUR GUARDS--I DON'T WANT YOU TRAVELING ALONE.
THANK YOU, FATHER, FOR MAKING ME PROUD.

I'M SORRY YOU HAD TO SUFFER LIKE THAT. CORUSCANT SEEMS TO REPRESENT WHAT THE ENTIRE GALAXY IS BECOMING, I'M AFRAID.

WHY DID YOU RISK YOUR OWN SAFETY TO HELP ME? YOU DON'T EVEN KNOW ME.

BECAUSE EVERY LIFE HAS VALUE AND IS DESERVING OF PRESERVATION.
I CAME TO CORUSCANT THINKING IT AN EXOTIC, ENTICING PLACE. INSTEAD, I'VE FOUND THAT ITS EXTERIOR BEAUTY HIDES A VERY UGLY TRUTH.
WE ARE NOT ALL BAD. I INTEND TO PROVE THAT. FIRST IMPRESSIONS CAN BE MISLEADING SOMETIMES.

INDEED THEY CAN. BUT IN THIS CASE, YOU HAVE PROVEN TO BE AS KIND AS YOU ARE BRAVE. IT WILL BE LONG REMEMBERED. BY MYSELF AND MY PEOPLE.
I AM EG'ROS AKALA.

LEIA ORGANA.

VERY NICE TO MEET YOU, LEIA ORGANA.

End

MOS EISLEY, TATOOINE
LUKE SKYWALKER, YOUR TICKET TO THE STARS...

WOW! I STILL CAN'T BELIEVE THIS IS FINALLY HAPPENING!
HEY, WHEN BIGGS DARKLIGHTER PROMISES, HE DELIVERS.
WE'RE HEADED INTO SPACE, FARMBOY!

I ONLY WISH IT COULD'VE BEEN FARTHER OUT...THE MOON WILL HAVE TO DO WITH WHAT LITTLE CREDS WE HAVE.
IT'S MY LANDSPEEDER SAVINGS, BUT IT'LL BE WORTH IT!
I'M TIRED OF LOOKING AT THE GALAXY THROUGH MACRO-BINOCULARS...
LUKE, M'BOY --
--THERE SHE IS! A CONVERTED GALLOFREE, LOOKS LIKE.
KIND OF AN OLDER MODEL...
SHE'S...SHE'S BEAUTIFUL!

# FALLING STAR

HAVE ANY TROUBLE GETTING THE TICKETS?
NO, AS USUAL, CREDITS TALK. THEY DON'T REALLY CARE IF A COUPLE OF JUVES WANT TO GO TO THE MOON.
THEY'LL BARELY NOTICE US AMONG ALL THE MINERS AND SALESMEN AND WHATEVER...
FIND A SEAT AND STRAP IN... DON'T TOUCH NUTHIN'.
THIS IS JUST ABOUT EVERYTHING I'VE EVER DREAMED OF, BIGGS --
--TO GET OFF THIS ROCK, EVEN FOR A FEW HOURS!
HEY, LET'S GRAB THESE, BEFORE SOMEONE ELSE DOES...
OKAY! I GET THE VIEWPORT!
OOF!! HEY!!
ZUHFRAY...
THEY'RE REALLY PACKING 'EM IN ON THIS TUB!
HOW MUCH TIME UNTIL LIFTOFF? HOW LONG UNTIL WE HIT OUTER ORBIT? WHAT ABOUT...
OH, MAN!

WE CAN GET A PHIZZ AT THE MOONPORT, MAYBE TRY OUT SOME PRESSURE SUITS --
--SUPPOSEDLY THERE'S THIS NULL-GRAV ARCADE...
BIGGS!

WE'VE GOT TO REMEMBER TO PICK UP SOME POWER CONVERTERS AT TOSCHE STATION ON THE WAY BACK!
THAT'S WHERE I TOLD MY UNCLE WE'D BE. HE'D LOSE IT IF HE KNEW THE TRUTH.
YEAH, I'VE NOTICED. WHAT'S HIS DEAL? WHY DOES HE KEEP YOU SO...

LOCKED DOWN? I... I DUNNO.
IT'S A WONDER HE EVEN LETS ME LEAVE THE FARM. HE GETS ALL NERVOUS AND... ANGRY WHEN I BARELY MENTION SPACE OR STARPILOTS --
--OR MY FATHER.

S'ALMOST LIKE...LIKE HE DOESN'T WANT YOU TO LEAVE. LEAVE TATOOINE. OR SOMETHING.
DOESN'T MATTER, BIGGS.

UNCLE OWEN MAY BE LOCKED DOWN TO THIS PLANET --
-- BUT I'M NOT.

I CAN HEAR THE LIFTERS CHARGING...
THERE GOES THE PILOT. WE SHOULD BE GETTING UNDER WAY.

WHAAAAA-HOOOOO!!!

SORRY 'BOUT THE BUMPY RIDE, SIR!
IT'S GREAT! GREAT! I LOVE IT!
SPACE, HERE I COME!

STILL HAVE A FEW LAYERS OF ATMOSPHERE TO GET THROUGH, FARMBOY!
BUT YOU SHOULD BE SEEING THE UPPER STRATA SOON...

HEH, SOUNDS LIKE YOU'RE WRITING YOUR ACADEMY APPLICATION A BIT EARLY, BIGGS...

IT'S GETTING KINDA HOT --
-- SHIELDS SHOULD BE ABSORBING THAT.
LUKE SKYWALKER, STARPILOT! ON HIS FIRST, BUT ABSOLUTELY NOT LAST, JOURN...

BAROOOMM!!!
NOOOOO!!!
NO! THIS CAN'T BE HAPPENING!
LUKE! LUKE, WE'RE FINE! WE'LL BE FINE --
-- AS LONG AS NO ONE --
--PANICS...

WE'RE STARTING TO DROP...WE'LL BURN UP IN A MATTER OF MINUTES, LUKE...

NOT SURE WHAT TO DO. TOO CRAZY IN HERE...
CAN'T BELIEVE THIS IS HAPPENING...

UHHHH!!!
NYYY! NYYYY!
BIGGS!

BLAST IT, BIGGS, ARE YOU OKAY?!?
UHHHH...FELT BETTER...

GOT A BAD FEELING 'BOUT THI...
DON'T SAY IT!
DO SUMTHIN'...

I WILL.

...WORTHLESS PIECE OF KRAYT OFFAL! PANEL'S BLOWN! WHATTA MESS...

HUH. THIS DOESN'T LOOK SO BAD. YOU'VE GOTTA...
WHAT???

WHAT ARE YOU DOIN', BOY!? GET YOURSELF RIGHT BACK DOWN THAT LADDER! I'M--

LOOK, YOU'VE JUST GOTTA REROUTE THESE CIRCUITS AND BACK-ARC THE --
STOP RIGHT THERE! GET AWAY FROM THAT!
NO FARM-SCRAP'S GONNA TELL ME! I'LL--

LET HIM TRY. BLAST IT, YOU'VE GOT NOTHING TO LOSE BY LETTING HIM TRY!
LUKE, DON'T FORGET THE --
I KNOW! I KNOW!

CONCENTRATE, CONCENTRATE...
DEFUSE --
-- DISCONNECT --
-- REROUTE --
-- RECONNECT --
-- REPOWER --
-- ONLINE?
TRY IT! TRY IT!

THAT'S DONE IT, LAD! SHIELDS BACK ONLINE, CONVERTERS FIRING!
GOOD! WE CAN GET BACK ON COURSE!

WHAT ARE YOU GOIN' ON ABOUT?
THE TRIP...TO THE MOON...

WE'RE HEADING BACK, BOY! I'M NOT RISKING MY LIFE AND EVERYONE ELSE'S FOR YOUR LITTLE HOLIDAY!
NO...

LATER...
WHAT A KID!
I KNEW THE BOY COULD DO IT!
ALQUONO DEG APPREFARON.
NEVER BEEN SO SCARED...
THANK YOU, LADDIE!
BLESS YOU, SON...
...FEET ON SOLID GROUND!
C'MON, LUKE. LET'S TRY AN' GET OUR CREDITS BACK...
NO --

-- WE'VE... I'VE GOT TO GET **HOME**.

THERE YOU **ARE**, LUKE. SUPPER'S ALMOST READY. GO AND **CLEAN UP**. YOU LOOK ALL **SOOTY**.
HOW WAS **TOSCHE STATION**?
IT --
LUKE, I HAVE A FEW **CHORES** FOR YOU... **RIGHT** AFTER SUPPER, YOU START IN ON 'EM.
-- WAS --
YOU **HEAR** ME?
YOU **DRAG** YOUR FEET LIKE **THAT**, ALL YOU'LL DO IS KICK UP **SAND**.
-- FINE.

MAYBE DRAG MY FEET HERE IS ALL I WAS EVER MEANT TO DO, UNCLE OWEN...
THE END.

# Do or Do Not

DO OR DO NOT
I MEAN, SURE, THE EMPEROR IS DEAD, BUT WHO'S GOING TO DO ALL OF THE CLEANUP?

EVERYONE THINKS IT'S SO GREAT THAT WE WON, BUT LOOK WHAT WE GOT OUT OF IT--A WHOLE GALAXY TO REBUILD.

WHY DID YOU LEAVE ME HERE? DO YOU HAVE SOME PLACE BETTER TO BE?!

I'D BETTER GO HAVE A TALK WITH HIM.

ARE YOU OKAY?

FINE, REALLY, FINE.
WHO WERE YOU TALKING TO JUST NOW?

NO ONE.
OKAY...?

IN THE LAST FEW DAYS, EVER SINCE WE DEFEATED THE EMPEROR, THE OLD JEDI MASTERS HAVE STOPPED TALKING TO ME.
NOW I HAVE NO IDEA WHAT TO DO.

MAYBE THAT'S BECAUSE YOU DON'T NEED TO BE DOING ANYTHING NOW.

I'VE BEEN DOING SOMETHING EVERY DAY FOR OVER FIVE YEARS.
AND NOW I'VE GOT TO REBUILD THE JEDI ORDER ALL BY MYSELF!

I'M SORRY I HAVEN'T BEEN PAYING SO MUCH ATTENTION, WITH THINGS GOING ON WITH--
WITH HAN, I KNOW. GUESS THINGS ARE GETTING SERIOUS?

KIND OF.

SO... YOU'RE OKAY?

I DON'T KNOW. I MEAN, HE'S A GREAT GUY, BUT HE'S--
NOT GOOD ENOUGH FOR YOUR SISTER?

NO! NO! I MEAN--

I MEAN, JUST A FEW YEARS AGO I WAS GOING TO BE THIS HOTSHOT FIGHTER PILOT DEFENDING THE GALAXY WITH A BEAUTIFUL PRINCESS AT MY SIDE--

GO ON...

I JUST HAVEN'T HAD TIME TO FIGURE OUT EVERYTHING ABOUT WHO I AM--THE LAST JEDI, YOUR BROTHER...

YOU'RE NOT ALONE, YOU KNOW.

I KNOW. AND HEY, MAYBE YOU AND HAN WILL MAKE SOME LITTLE JEDI FOR ME TO TRAIN SOME DAY.
MAYBE.

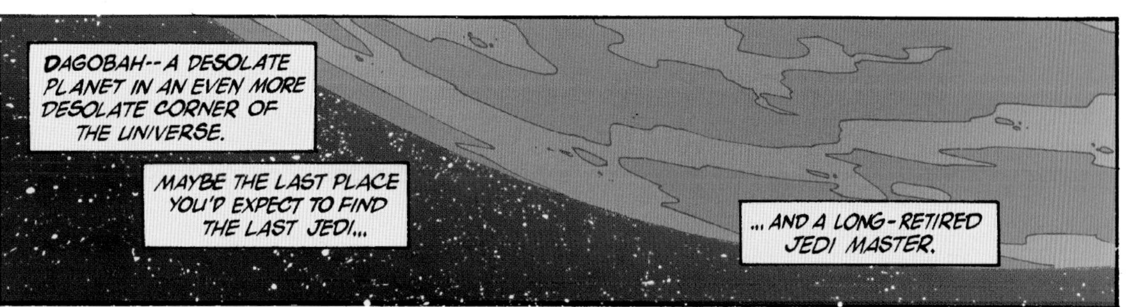
DAGOBAH--A DESOLATE PLANET IN AN EVEN MORE DESOLATE CORNER OF THE UNIVERSE.
MAYBE THE LAST PLACE YOU'D EXPECT TO FIND THE LAST JEDI...
...AND A LONG-RETIRED JEDI MASTER.

WHICH IS WHY IT WAS THE PERFECT PLACE FOR YOUNG LUKE SKYWALKER TO LEARN THE WAYS OF THE FORCE FROM YODA.
PERFECT, UNTIL FIVE MINUTES AGO.

SLIPPERY SLOPE

I'VE GOT A BAD FEELING ABOUT THIS.

BUT BAD FEELING OR NOT--I'VE GOT TO STOP THAT MAN!
HERE GOES... NOTHING.

GRASP!

PLUMMETING TO CERTAIN DEATH, LUKE REMAINS IMPRESSIVELY CALM--

--CONCENTRATING.

HE'S NOT READY TO DIE THIS DAY.

NOT HERE.

NOT NOW.

APPARENTLY...
FLIP
GRAB

...THE FORCE CONCURS.
Phew.

FOR LUKE SKYWALKER KNOWS HE HAS BECOME THE NEW HOPE FOR FREEDOM IN A GALAXY THREATENED BY THE DEATH GRIP OF A DESPOTIC EMPIRE.
HE HAS A PEOPLE TO FREE--
--FAMILY AND FRIENDS TO AVENGE.

NOTHING WILL JEOPARDIZE HIS GOALS.
NO ONE WILL.

HOW MUCH... LONGER DO I NEED TO STAY LIKE THIS?
HOW MUCH WANT YOU TO STAY LIKE THAT?
LONGER AND WORK-- OR GIVE UP NOW AND REST?
Hmm?
I DIDN'T SAY ANYTHING ABOUT GIVING UP!
WHO SAID ANY--?!
Shh.
VISITOR IN A PLACE WHERE THERE SHOULD NOT BE!
STOPPED, MUST HE BE!
DO NOT LET HIM ESCAPE TO TELL THE TALE!
IF OUR SECRET IS LOST, THEN GALAXY IS LOST AS WELL!
I UNDERSTAND, MASTER!

HA! PERFECT-- WHOEVER IT WAS HASN'T LEFT YET!
AND JUDGING BY THE LOOKS OF THAT SCOUT SHIP...

DON'T DISPARAGE THE SHIP, BOY.
CH-CHAKT

I'LL BE TRADING IT IN AFTER I GET THE EMPIRE'S REWARD FOR BRINGING YOU IN DEAD OR ALIVE...
...OR MAYBE I'LL BLACKMAIL THE ALLIANCE TO KEEP YOUR WHEREABOUTS A SECRET.

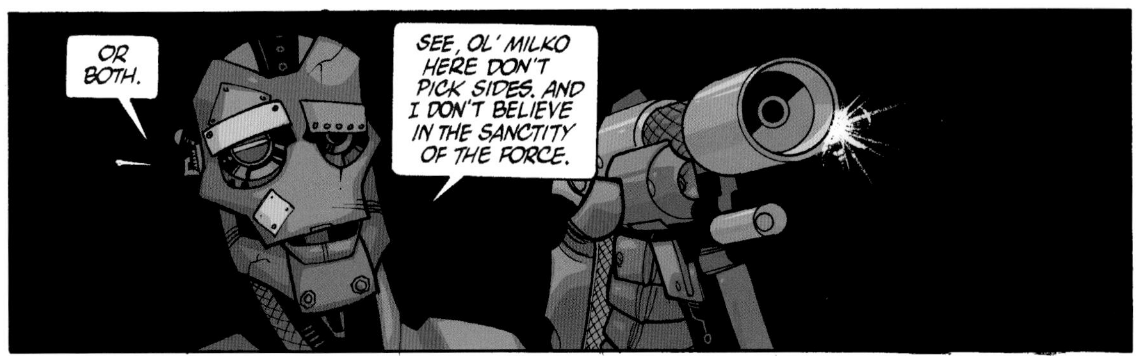
OR BOTH.
SEE, OL' MILKO HERE DON'T PICK SIDES. AND I DON'T BELIEVE IN THE SANCTITY OF THE FORCE.

YOU DON'T HAVE TO BELIEVE IN THE FORCE...

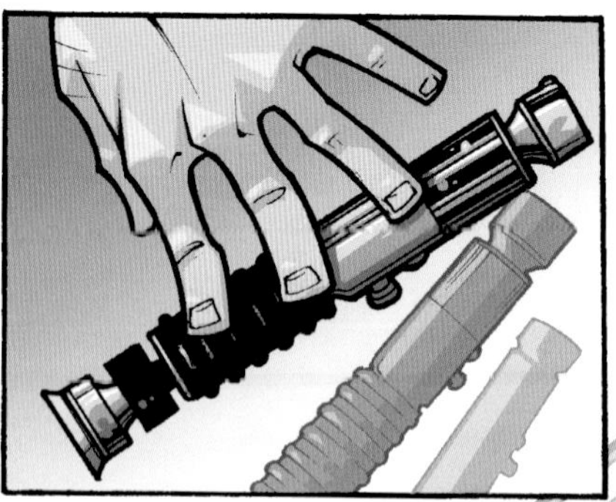

...IT IS ENOUGH THAT I DO.
VMMM

SEE?
ULP.

OH, PLEASE BENEFICIAL AND MAGNIFICENT JEDI PRIEST PLEASE SPARE MY WORTHLESS LIFE I PROMISE...

NOW WHAT?

...HAVE EIGHT KIDS TO TAKE CARE OF AND A SICK MOTHER ON DANCHIAN PRIME...

I CAN'T JUST LET HIM GO--AND NO WAY AM I FAR ENOUGH ALONG IN MY TRAINING TO MENTALLY REWIRE HIS MIND LIKE OBI-WAN COULD.

AND I'M SURE YODA'S A GOOD CENTURY TOO OLD TO PULL IT OFF.

BUT I CAN'T KILL THIS BOUNTY HUNTER JUST TO KEEP A SECRET.

OR CAN I?

DO I HAVE A CHOICE?

...PROMISE TO FEED ORPHANS AND CLOTHE THE POOR AND...

ENOUGH.

YOU'RE GOING TO LIVE THIS DAY, MILKO.

LEAVE, KNOWING YOUR LIFE WON'T BE WORTH A HANDFUL OF CREDITS AND YOUR REPUTATION WILL BE SHATTERED--

--ONCE IT GETS OUT THAT YOU GOT THE DROP ON A JEDI KNIGHT AND THEN HAD TO BEG FOR YOUR LIFE.

?
MAY... THE... FORCE... BE... WITH... YOU...
AND... WITH YOU.

INTIMIDATE HIM, YOU DID.
APPEAL TO HIS VANITY, YOU DID.
INTERESTING CHOICE.

WOULD NOT HAVE WORKED IN MY TIME.
COME-- MUCH MORE TO BE LEARNED.
MUCH.
WHY DOES IT FEEL LIKE I JUST PASSED ANOTHER ONE OF HIS TESTS?

OR DID I FAIL?
Hmm.

END

THE PLANET ELERION, SOMEWHERE IN THE OUTER RIM.
VISITORS COME HERE FOR ONE REASON...
...TO GAMBLE.
SOME WITH THEIR FORTUNES...OTHERS WITH THEIR LIVES.
Lucky Stars
WELCOME TO ELERION, PRINCESS LEIA. WE'RE GLAD YOU COULD MAKE IT HERE SO QUICKLY.
OF COURSE. IT'S VITAL I MAKE SURE THIS MISSION IS A SUCCESS. YOU'RE GENERAL HUNDEEN--?
I AM. NOW, LET'S GET YOU BRIEFED...

FEEL FREE TO CALL ME ORMA...RANK DOESN'T CARRY MUCH WEIGHT HERE...
IF IT DID, THE WEIGHT WOULD EVAPORATE IN THIS HEAT AND HUMIDITY. HOW DO YOU STAND IT?
YOU GET USED TO IT.
PRINCESS LEIA, ALLOW ME TO PRESENT THE TROOPS YOU'LL BE WORKING WITH--MY BEST AGENTS...
ZEELA NALL.
NURI PRAVADA.
SHEYNE TYNDOS.
PLEASED TO MEET YOU... PRINCESS.
...
CALL ME LEIA, PLEASE.
I'M PLEASED TO MEET YOU ALL.
NOW, AS TO WHY YOU'RE HERE...
YES, THE STOLEN DATA REVEALING THE LOCATION OF THE MAIN REBEL BASES...

THE THIEVES, AS YOU KNOW, THEY KILLED A REBEL COURIER ON FARWELL STATION AND STOLE THE HOLOCUBE MAP.
THEY'VE MADE ARRANGEMENTS TO SELL THE HOLOCUBE TO THE EMPIRE HERE ON ELERION-- AT KUSHAL VOGH.
RIGHT. I'VE BEEN ON THEIR... um... TAIL SINCE PHOEBUS. KUSHAL VOGH IS THE GAMBLING CENTER, YES?
AT LEAST. IT IS A WIDE-OPEN, LAWLESS PLACE.
THE IMPERIAL AGENTS ARRIVE TODAY, AND WE EXPECT THE TRANSFER TONIGHT.
OBVIOUSLY, WE CAN'T ALLOW THAT.
WE NEED TO GET YOU FOUR INSIDE TO SHUT THEM DOWN.
WE'LL START BY KEEPING THE TWO PARTIES SEPARATE UNTIL YOU LOCATE THE HOLOCUBE.
ME?
OKAY, HOW DO I GET CLOSE?
WE'RE GOING UNDERCOVER...
...THE RED ONE'S YOURS.
THERE'S NO WAY I'LL WEAR THAT--!

ALL RIGHT, I'M IN. NOW WHAT?

YOU LOCATE THE THIEVES AND RETRIEVE THE HOLO-CUBE...
LUCKY STAR

...HOW IS UP TO YOU.
THE OTHERS WILL WATCH FOR THE IMPERIALS... AND WAYLAY THEM.

GOOD HUNTING.
YEAH-- WULUPP!

YOU OKAY, THERE, DARLIN'...? NAME'S SORN ARGOS... I JUST MADE PLANETFALL...

FORGET IT, HOTSHOT, SPACE JOCKEYS AREN'T MY TYPE.
NOW IF YOU'LL EXCUSE ME, I SEE SOMEONE I KNOW...

EXCUSE ME--? GENTLEMEN--?
WHAT'S HE GOT THAT I DON'T...?
I DON'T BELIEVE I'VE EVER SEEN ANYONE SO... TALL...
DON'T WASTE YOUR TIME ON HERMOS, BEAUTIFUL, HE'S JUST A BODYGUARD...
...AND AN ANDROID TO BOOT.
I AM NESCAN TAL'YO, FREELANCE... IMPORT EXPERT. I AM SO GLAD TO MAKE YOUR ACQUAINTANCE, BEAUTIFUL HUMAN. YOU ARE...?
LEI-- CALL ME LENA. WHERE ARE WE GOING?
TO PLAY... BUT NOT AT THE GAMING TABLES, eh?
"MUCH MORE FUN TO BE HAD... UP IN MY ROOM..."

WHAT A DECADENT MESS! LET'S FIND THE WEASEL AND GET BACK TO THE TRANSPORT.
BUT COMMANDER SHAD, CERTAINLY THE EMPIRE WILL NOT BEGRUDGE US SOME RELAXATION?
PERHAPS NOT, MORELY, BUT I WOULD. I DON'T WANT MY JUNIOR OFFICERS TOO RELAXED. WE ARE AT WAR, AFTER ALL.
BESIDES, WHAT COULD THIS BACKWATER DUMP HAVE TO INTRIGUE OUR SUPERIOR TASTES?
Oh, GENTLE-MEN...

I TOLD YOU GIRLS, DIDN'T I? I SAID THERE HAD TO BE REAL MEN HERE...!
YOUNG LADY, I DON'T...

DON'T BE MODEST. I CAN TELL A SOPHISTICATED MAN OF THE GALAXY WHEN I MEET ONE! SO VIRILE AND HANDSOME!
ME...? Heh-heh-heh-heh... oh...

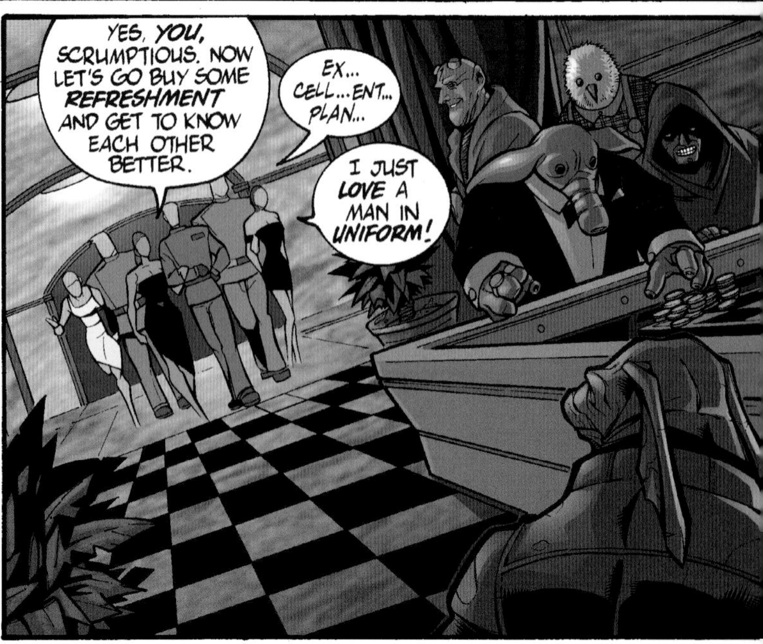

YES, YOU, SCRUMPTIOUS. NOW LET'S GO BUY SOME REFRESHMENT AND GET TO KNOW EACH OTHER BETTER.
EX... CELL...ENT... PLAN...
I JUST LOVE A MAN IN UNIFORM!

COME ON NOW, NESCAN, LET'S NOT RUSH THINGS...
ONCE WE GET STARTED, I'LL TAKE THINGS NICE AND SLOW, I PROMISE!
THIS IS YOUR LUCKY NIGHT, MY DEAR...
TO BE IN THE COMPANY OF SUCH A GREAT SENTIENT? I'M SURE...
OH--?
Oh, BUT AS OF TODAY I AM AN INCREDIBLY WEALTHY ONE, TOO!
AND POWERFUL TOO, NOW THAT I THINK OF IT.
YOU'RE LOOKING AT THE BEING WHO HOLDS THE FATE OF THE REBELLION IN HIS VERY PAW!
AND THE EMPIRE IS PAYING A PLANETARY FORTUNE FOR WHAT I HAVE TO SELL.
NO.
I WANT THAT HOLOCUBE RIGHT NOW, WEASEL!
Oh, DRAT. HERMOS.

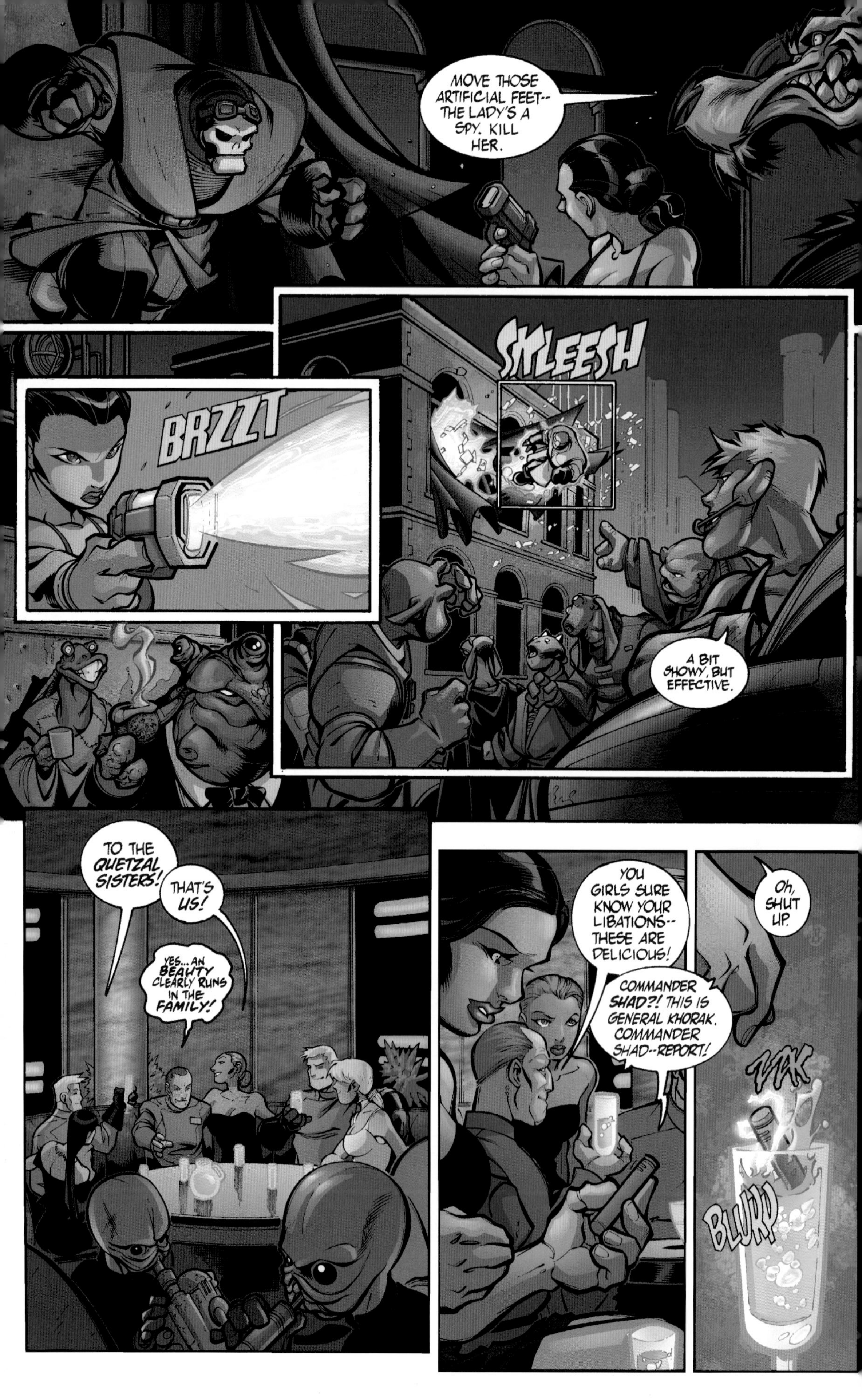

MOVE THOSE ARTIFICIAL FEET-- THE LADY'S A SPY. KILL HER.

BRZZT

SKLEESH

A BIT SHOWY, BUT EFFECTIVE.

OKAY, ORMA... GOT IT.
FOLD UP THE CIRCUS, LADIES! THE PRINCESS IS ONTO THE CUBE-- WE'RE OUTTA HERE!
GOOD NIGHT, BOYS...
A TRICK! STOP THEM, MEN!
YOU'LL ANSWER FOR THIS, YOU FLOOZIES!
NICE TALK.
SHRAK
THWAKA
SECURITY!
QUIET DOWN!
HEADS UP, LADIES... A SQUADRON OF STORMTROOPERS IS ON ITS WAY TO RESCUE YOUR BOYFRIENDS!

FORGET IT, LADY... I'VE NOTHING TO SAY.
EVEN IF YOU KILL ME, THE HOLOCUBE STILL GETS TO THE EMPIRE, AND YOUR PRECIOUS REBELS ARE DOOMED!
OKAY, I BELIEVE YOU'RE NOT AFRAID TO DIE...
...HOW ARE YOU AT HANDLING... PAIN?
NOW, NOW... LET'S NOT BE HASTY...
THE HOLO-CUBE?
ALL RIGHT... BUT I DON'T HAVE IT. IT'S WITH MY PARTNER...
...GOGOL, THE CASINO OWNER!
WE CAN SHARE, THOUGH-- THERE'LL BE CREDITS ENOUGH FOR ALL OF US TO LIVE LIKE PASHAS!
NOW, WHY NOT UNTIE ME? UNLESS YOU LIKE THIS SORT OF THING?
Oh, SHUT UP.
THWAK

ORMA, I'M ON MY WAY TO THE HOLOCUBE. THE CASINO OWNER'S IN ON IT.
GOT IT-- BUT BE AWARE, STORMTROOPERS ARE ON THEIR WAY.
THEY'RE WORRIED ABOUT THEIR OFFICERS...

KRESHH
CAD! HOW DARE YOU TAKE ADVANTAGE OF A HELPLESS GIRL LIKE ME?
WANTED TO SHOW ME HIS "ART" HOLOS!
HOW DÉCLASSÉ!

OKAY, WE RENDEZVOUS WITH THE PRINCESS AND GET OUT FAST!

I THINK YOU HAVE THE WRONG DOOR, MY DEAR...
...THOUGH PERHAPS *FATE* HAS BROUGHT US TOGETHER--?
*WHAT* IS IT WITH YOU GUYS?
WHAT CAN I SAY? NOW, WHAT'S THIS ABOUT?
IT'S ABOUT YOU GIVING ME THE *HOLOCUBE,* GOGOL--BEFORE I *TOAST* YOUR TAIL!
*Oh, I SEE...*
SEE WHAT? WHERE'S THE HOLOCUBE?
IT'S RIGHT *HERE* IN FRONT OF YOU!
IT'S HIDDEN UP THERE IN PLAIN SIGHT... BUT YOU'LL NEVER FIND IT IN A MILLION YEARS!
YOU MIS-UNDERSTAND. I DON'T *NEED* TO FIND IT...

SKLESH
...I JUST NEED TO SEE THAT NO ONE ELSE DOES!
THAT CUBE WAS WORTH THOUSANDS OF CREDITS! NOW IT'S... IT'S...
SLAG.
WELL... TIME FOR ME TO BE GOING.
OF COURSE, I WAS NEVER HERE.
I WISH I COULD SAY THE SAME. THE EMPIRE'S GOING TO CRUSH ME...
Whew, I SMELL TOASTED HOLOCUBE... EVERYTHING GOOD?
BETTER, EVEN. LET'S GO.
THIS WAY, MEN, HURRY!

Ooh, LOOK AT THE PRETTY SOLDIERS!
I AM GENERAL KHORAK. WHERE ARE MY MEN?
YES, SIR... THEY, WERE, ah, THAT IS... A GROUP OF...
A GROUP OF REBEL TERRORISTS, SIR...
...WAYLAID US AND DESTROYED THE HOLOCUBE, SIR... MUST'VE BEEN... SIX HEAVILY ARMED MEN...
MORE LIKE TEN, ACTUALLY.
MAYBE EVEN TWELVE. THEY WERE BRUTES!
LUCKY STAR
PUT OUT AN ALERT WITH FULL DESCRIPTIONS! THIS FACILITY IS CLOSED INDEFINITELY!
MISSION ACCOMPLISHED, GENERAL--THANKS TO YOU AND YOUR... SPECIAL SQUAD!
NICE WORKING WITH YOU LADIES.
YES, LET'S DO IT AGAIN SOME-TIME...
END

The Other
CORUSCANT--
CENTER OF THE
NEW REPUBLIC.
WHOOPS!
--YOU DO REALIZE THAT ONCE YOU TAKE ON THIS ALL-ENCOMPASSING ROLE, YOU'LL BASICALLY BE TURNING YOUR BACK ON ANY CHANCE OF EVER BECOMING A JEDI.
BOTH THINGS ARE NOT POSSIBLE.
YOUR SUPER SOARAWAY
HOLO NEWS
SAM ON VID 3
ORGANA-SOLO TO BE SWORN IN AS PRESIDENT TODAY
WIN TICKETS
>MORE<
LUKE...
...I HAVE VERY CONSCIOUSLY CHOSEN MY POLITICAL CAREER. I HAVE A FAMILY I NEED TO TAKE CARE OF AND--
WHEN YOUR PREDECESSOR STEPS DOWN DUE TO A NEAR-FATAL ASSASSINATION ATTEMPT, RUSHING TO TAKE HER PLACE MAY NOT BE THE SAFEST ROAD TRAVELED...
NICE!
...ESPECIALLY WITH CHILDREN TO CARE FOR.
AND WOULD THE LIFE OF A JEDI BE ANY SAFER?
NO... I SUPPOSE NOT...

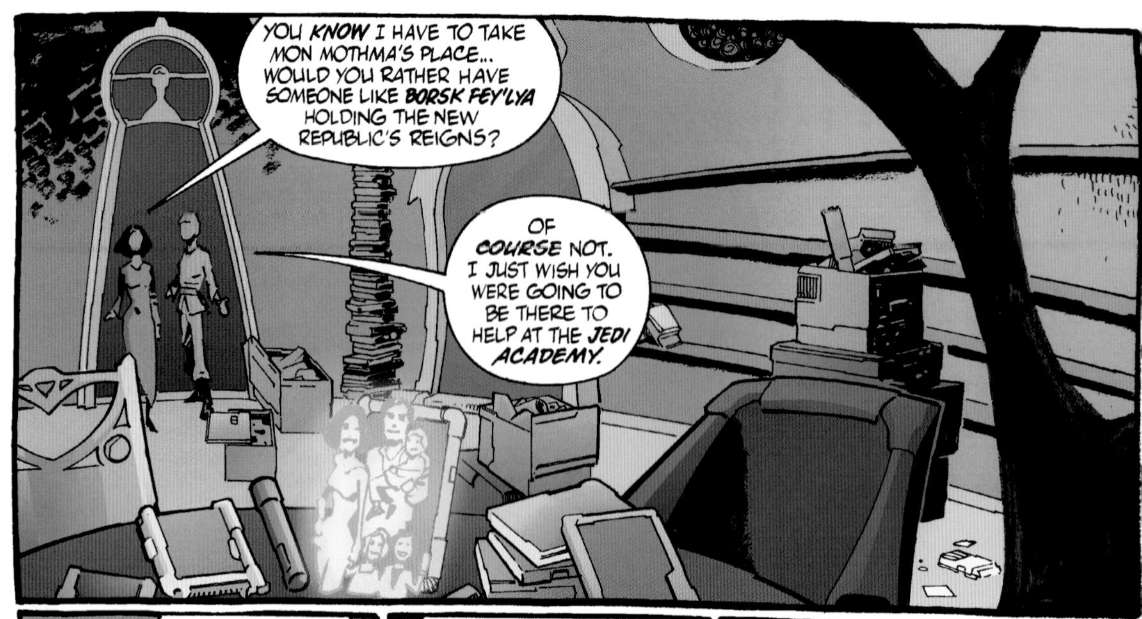
YOU KNOW I HAVE TO TAKE MON MOTHMA'S PLACE... WOULD YOU RATHER HAVE SOMEONE LIKE BORSK FEY'LYA HOLDING THE NEW REPUBLIC'S REIGNS?
OF COURSE NOT. I JUST WISH YOU WERE GOING TO BE THERE TO HELP AT THE JEDI ACADEMY.

IF YOU ONLY TOOK THE TIME TO TRAIN HARDER.
I'M CONFIDENT YOU CAN HANDLE THE TRAINING OF THE NEW JEDI YOURSELF--DON'T WORRY!
WE SIMPLY HAVE DIFFERENT PATHS TO FOLLOW, AND EACH IS EQUALLY IMPORTANT TO THE GALAXY.

PLUS, WE BOTH KNOW I'VE REACHED SOME KIND OF BARRIER IN MY GROWTH AS A JEDI WHICH I CAN'T SEEM TO GET PAST.

YES... THE "BARRIER"...
AND DON'T SAY YOU'VE GOT A BAD FEELING ABOUT IT.
IF I HAD A CREDIT FOR EVERY TIME I'VE HEARD THAT...

:sigh: THREEPIO IS HELPING ME PACK.
Oh.
I'M SORRY.

I'LL SEE YOU AT THE CEREMONY--IF YOU CAN FIND YOUR WAY OUT OF THIS MESS...
MISTRESS LEIA!

Oh, DEAR!
MISTRESS LEIA, I'M **TERRIBLY** SORRY!
I WAS ONLY **MERELY** TRYING TO HELP!
**WHAT** WAS I **THINKING?** IT'S ALL **ARTOO'S** FAULT! I **NEVER** SHOULD HAVE LET **HIM** SUGGEST THA--
MY OLD DIARY...
KLIK

I HAVEN'T WRITTEN IN THIS FOR **YEARS...**
DID I **REALLY** DROP A WATER BALLOON ON **TARKIN'S HEAD? TWICE?!**

-:sigh:- ALDERAAN...

I wonder if I **have** made the right choice. I wish Father were here... he would know what to do.
He was always so **wise**.

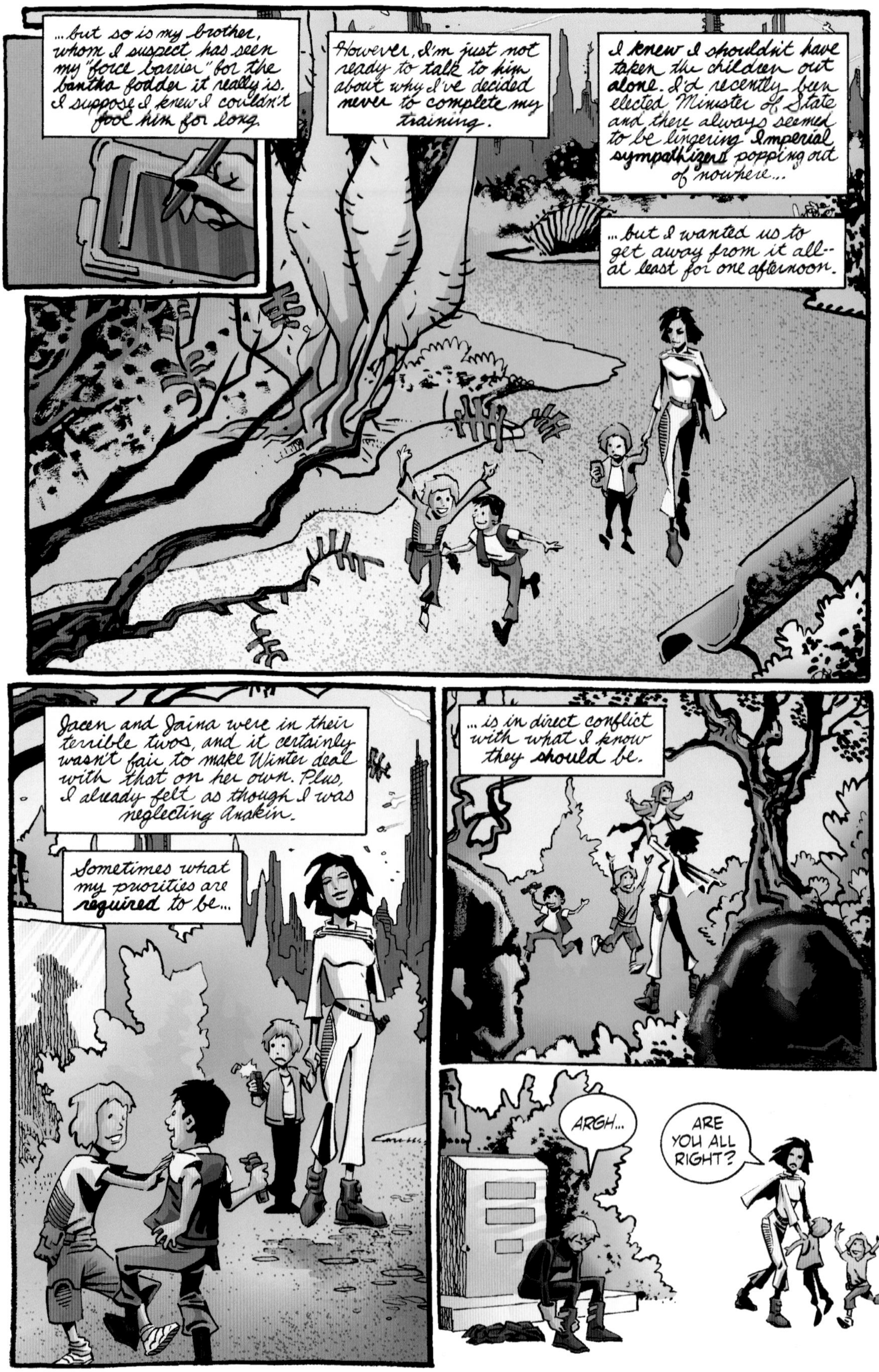

...but so is my brother, whom I suspect has seen my "force barrier" for the **bantha fodder** it really is. I suppose I knew I couldn't fool him for long.

However, I'm just not ready to talk to him about why I've decided **never** to complete my training.

**I knew** I shouldn't have taken the children out **alone**. I'd recently been elected Minister of State and there always seemed to be lingering **Imperial sympathizers** popping out of nowhere...

...but I wanted us to get away from it all--at least for one afternoon.

Jacen and Jaina were in their terrible twos, and it certainly wasn't fair to make Winter deal with that on her own. Plus, I already felt as though I was neglecting Anakin.
Sometimes what my priorities are **required** to be...
...is in direct conflict with what I know they **should** be.
ARGH...
ARE YOU ALL RIGHT?

SMACK

UGH!

NO!

*Even back then, I had already begun to shirk my Jedi training.*

HOLD IT **RIGHT** THERE, YOUR HIGHNESS!

*It wasn't like me to slack off on any endeavor...*

*...but there had always been something that felt "wrong" in the Force that I couldn't explain nor understand...*

VMMMM

I WILL **NOT** LET YOU HARM MY CHILDREN...

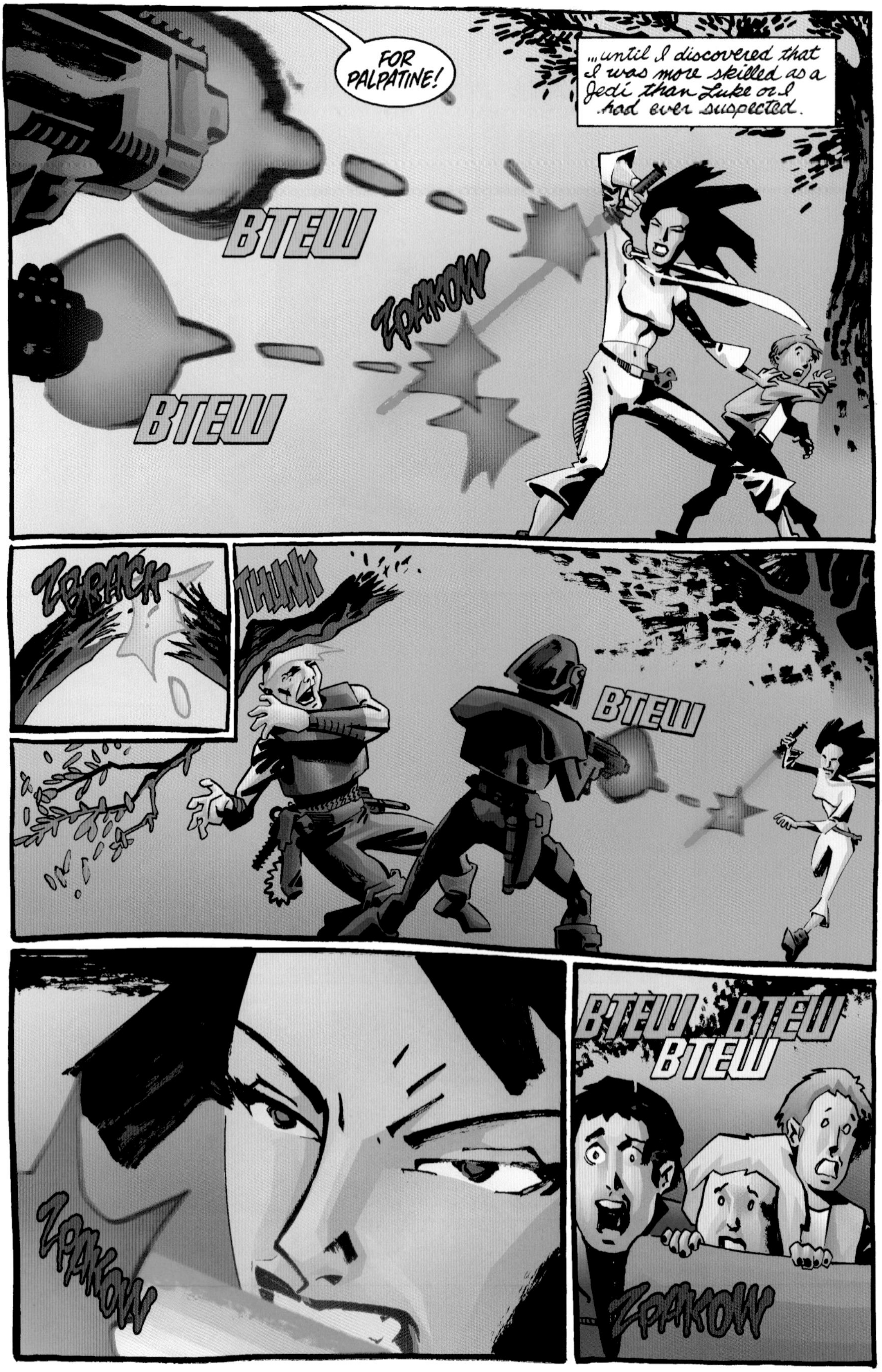

FOR PALPATINE!

...until I discovered that I was more skilled as a Jedi than Luke or I had ever suspected.

BTEW

ZPAKOW

BTEW

FVVST

BTEW
Despite the hours of instruction Luke had convinced me to endure, neither of us realized my full potential...
ZPAKKOW
AARGH
SLASH
...nor why I could never allow myself to reach it.

VADER...

At that moment, I looked into the face of the dark side... my dark side--and I understood his corruption.

FATHER.

It was then and there that I made the decision to avoid any possible temptation by the dark side and to make sure there was no chance of following in Vader's footsteps.

As a result, I decided to send the kids away with Winter to Anoth for safety...

...and threw myself head first deep into my political career...

...faking the "Force barrier" Luke recognized in me during our training--keeping him from discovering my true skill and potential...

...and thus terminating any chance of ever becoming a Jedi.

LET'S GO, SWEETHEART. IT'S TIME.
I had too much to lose...

I JUST WANTED YOU TO KNOW HOW PROUD I AM OF YOU...
...YOUR WORSHIPFUL-NESS.

I FORGOT TO WRITE SOME-THING DOWN. I'LL BE RIGHT THERE...
I may have given up the possibility of ever being a Jedi...
...but it could never compare to what I already have.
END

# BEST BIRTHDAY EVER!

WHY DIDN'T YOU JUST LET THEM DROP IT OFF?

THEY SAID THEY NEEDED JABBA'S SIGNATURE...

...AND HE'S NOT HERE!

OF *COURSE* HE'S NOT HERE, YOU DOLT!

JABBA TOOK VERY SPECIAL CARE TO BE AWAY FROM THE PALACE SO WE COULD PLAN FOR HIS PARTY!

AND HOW DO YOU THINK HE'LL FEEL IF EVERY SINGLE ONE OF HIS BIRTHDAY PRESENTS...

...IS NOT... PRESENT?

VERY ANGRY?

*INDEED!*

NOW ONE OF US IS GOING TO HAVE TO MAKE A SPECIAL TRIP INTO TOWN!

WELL, IT CAN'T BE ME...

*I* HAVE TO COORDINATE THE DANCE TROUPE WHEN THEY ARRIVE...

...*AND* I LEFT THE DECORATOR ALONE IN THE THRONE ROOM!

WELL *I* STILL NEED TO MEET WITH THE KITCHEN STAFF TO MAKE SURE ALL THE TASTERS HAVE MADE THEIR FINAL ARRANGEMENTS...

SANDS, SNAKES, AND SHARP-SHOOTERS?

Bah! ON THREE!

ONE!

HAHA

TWO!

Ffssht!

THREE!

TAKE MY SPEEDER!

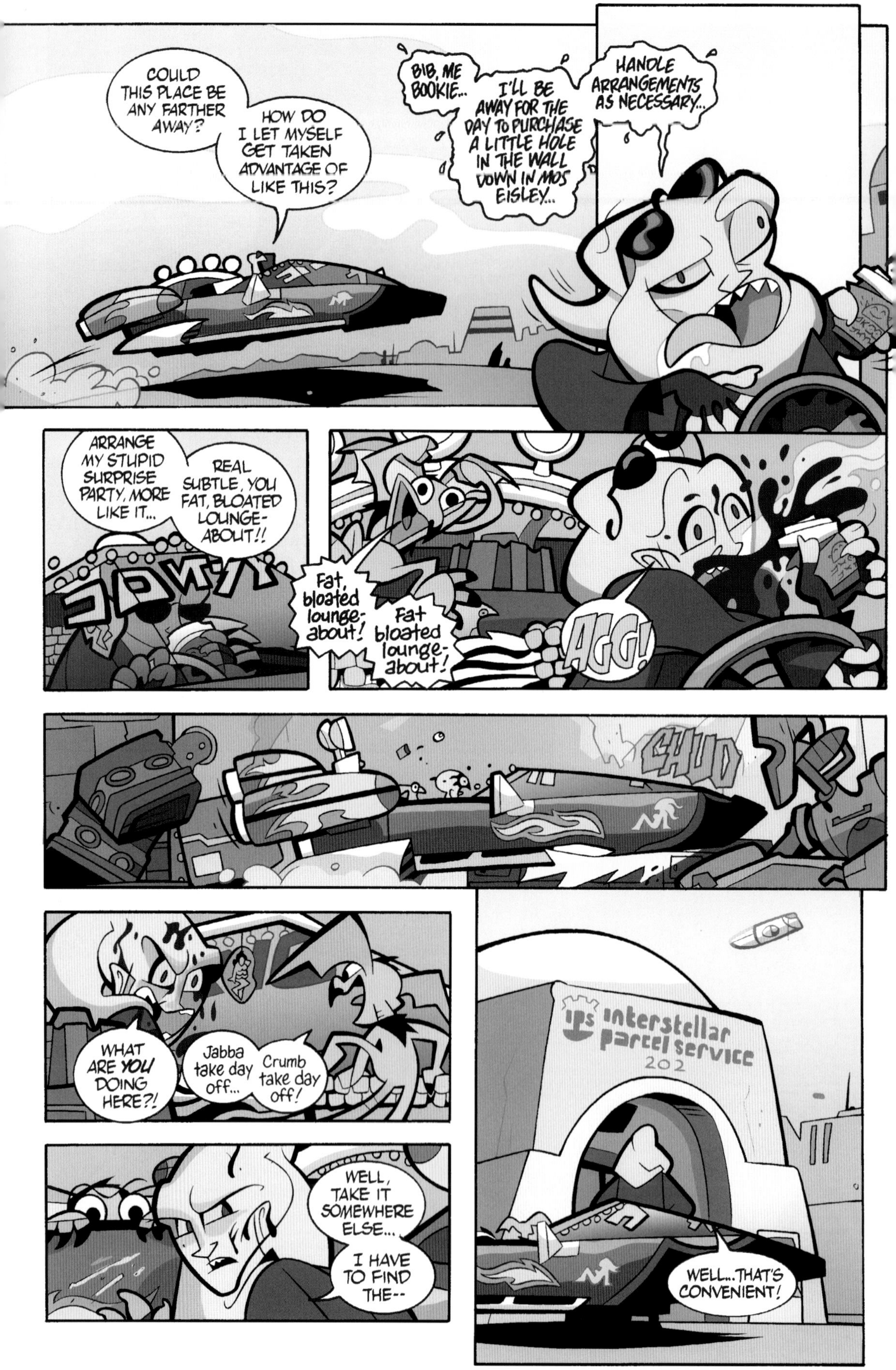

COULD THIS PLACE BE ANY FARTHER AWAY?
HOW DO I LET MYSELF GET TAKEN ADVANTAGE OF LIKE THIS?
BIB, ME BOOKIE...
I'LL BE AWAY FOR THE DAY TO PURCHASE A LITTLE HOLE IN THE WALL DOWN IN MOS EISLEY...
HANDLE ARRANGEMENTS AS NECESSARY...

ARRANGE MY STUPID SURPRISE PARTY, MORE LIKE IT...
REAL SUBTLE, YOU FAT, BLOATED LOUNGE-ABOUT!!

Fat, bloated lounge-about!
Fat bloated lounge-about!
AGG!

NEXT!

I'M HERE TO RETRIEVE THIS PACKAGE.
ARE YOU JABBA THE HUTT?
NO...I'M HIS--

IF YOU ARE NOT JABBA THE HUTT, THEN WE WILL NOT BE ABLE TO SURRENDER THE PACKAGE TO YOU AT THIS TIME.
BUT I'M HIS PERSONAL ASSISTANT!
I.D. CARD?

JABBA
Criminal Syndicate, inc.
FORTUNA, BIB OLTWAXT
PERSONAL ASSISTANT TO JABBA THE HUTT.
CRIME LORD

I'LL HAVE TO ASK MY SUPERVISOR ABOUT THIS.

TAPPITY TAP TAP

IT'S NOT HERE.
NOT HERE? WHAT DO YOU MEAN "IT'S NOT HERE"?!

IT WAS SENT TO OUR OVERSIZED PACKAGE REDISTRIBUTION CENTER ON DUNE STREET!

THANK YOU SO MUCH FOR YOUR HELP!

DUNE STREET.
REDISTRIBUTION CENTER
...COULD HAVE BEEN THE THIRD DUNE TO THE LEFT IN THE DUNE SEA FOR AS EASY AS THAT WAS TO FIND!

I'M HERE FOR THIS PACKAGE!
ARE YOU JABBA THE HUTT?

YES.

"SIGN HERE AND PULL AROUND BACK."
LOT THIRTY-TWO...
LOT THIRTY-THREE...
LOT THIRTY-FOUR...
WAHAHA!
SHUT UP OR I'M MAKING YOU CARRY IT!
LIVE CARGO
CAUTIO
WHAT IS THIS THING?
I COULDN'T TELL YOU...
BUT IT TOOK EIGHT GAS GRENADES TO KNOCK IT OUT AND GET IT THIS FAR...
...BROUGHT DOWN A WHOLE EXPRESS FREIGHTER...
...ATE THE PILOT AND CREW AND SCARED THE STINK OFF A PACK OF JAWAS.
FRANKLY, I'M ANXIOUS TO BE RID OF IT!
ANXIOUS ENOUGH TO THROW IN A REPULSOR LIFT TO CART IT OFF WITH?
I'LL SEE WHAT I CAN DO.
C'MON, YOU WORTH-LESS TUB OF NUTS...
...IT'S BAD ENOUGH I GOTTA BE SEEN IN THIS RIDICULOUS SPEEDER...
...BUT NOW WE'LL HAVE TO CUT THROUGH BEGGAR'S CANYON IF WE HOPE TO GET BACK TO THE PALACE BEFORE DARK!
SCRAPE
SCRUDGE

SOON...
DO YOU KNOW WHERE WE ARE?
I DON'T KNOW WHERE WE ARE...
I REALLY WISH YOU HADN'T EATEN THE MAP...
NOW WE'LL NEVER MAKE IT HOME BEFORE LOCKDOWN!
YOU KNOW, IT'D BE JUST MY LUCK TO RUN INTO--
SANDPEOPLE!
CRASH
REEEOOAARRR!
THUD
WHUMP

SCHLOP
MORFLE
SKLITCH

UGH! REVOLTING CREATURES!

SO YOU'VE GOT A TASTE FOR JAWAS?
C'MON, CRUMB, I'VE GOT A PLAN!
TOSS
click
KER-SLAM

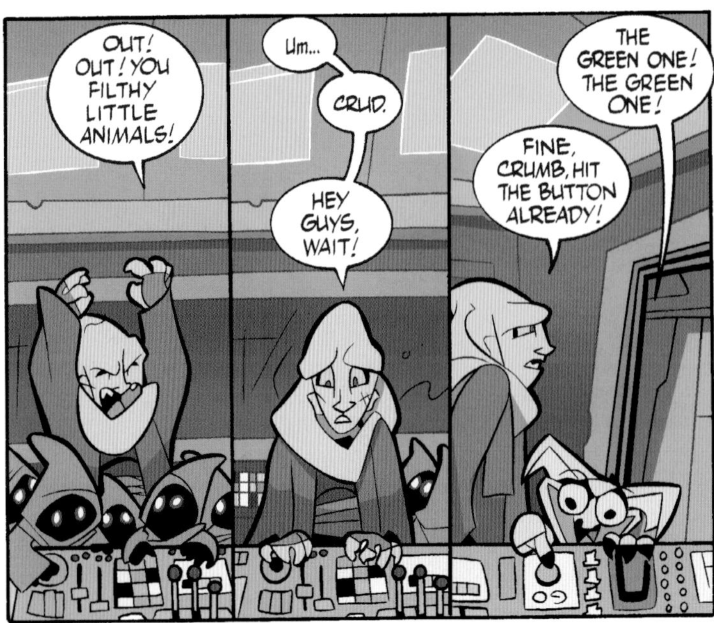
OUT! OUT! YOU FILTHY LITTLE ANIMALS!
Um...
CRUD.
HEY GUYS, WAIT!
THE GREEN ONE! THE GREEN ONE!
FINE, CRUMB, HIT THE BUTTON ALREADY!

RUMBLE RUMBLE
IS THAT IT?
IS THIS THING EVEN MOVING?
WE'RE DOOMED!
CHUG CHUG CHUG

CHUGGITA CHUGGITA PTHHH
ZIP
WHIRR
BEEP
LET US IN!
WHERE HAVE YOU BEEN?
I'VE BEEN BUSTING MY HUMP ALL NIGHT TRYING TO COVER FOR YOU!
YOU'LL BE ON JABBA'S HIT LIST FOR SURE MISSING CURFEW LIKE THAT!
WHERE'S MY SPEEDER?
I TRADED IT.
YOU... CIRCUS BOY! YOU'RE IN CHARGE OF THE MONSTER!
MONSTER?
WHEN'S THE BIG GUY GET BACK?
ANY MINUTE NOW.
WELL THEN WE'D BETTER GET TO THE THRONE ROOM!

THE THRONE ROOM.
SCUFFLE
QUIET!
SHHH!
SCUFFLE
OW! QUIT SHOVING!
snicker snicker
SCUFFLE
Shhh! HERE HE COMES!
SCHLUMPH
SCHLUMPH
SCHLUMPH
click
click
click
click
BIB?
BIB?
THE LIGHTS HAVE BURNT OUT AGAIN!
BIB?
NOW!

SURPRISE!
WHA?!

SCHOOMPH
BEEP

Hmm... DINNER AND A SHOW!
THIS IS THE BEST BIRTHDAY EVER!
SNORCHLE
MORGPH
CHRULP

THE END

# THE LONG, BAD DAY

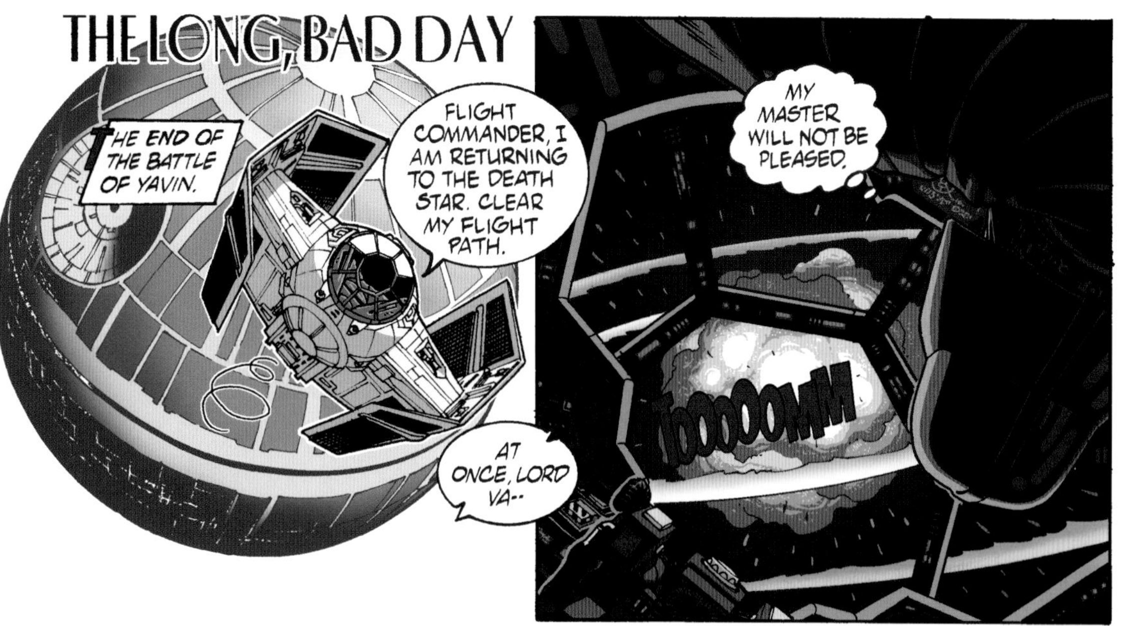

TH-
WACK
SHUT UP, OLD MAN!

GRAND MOFF TARKIN'S ESCAPE POD
FOOSH

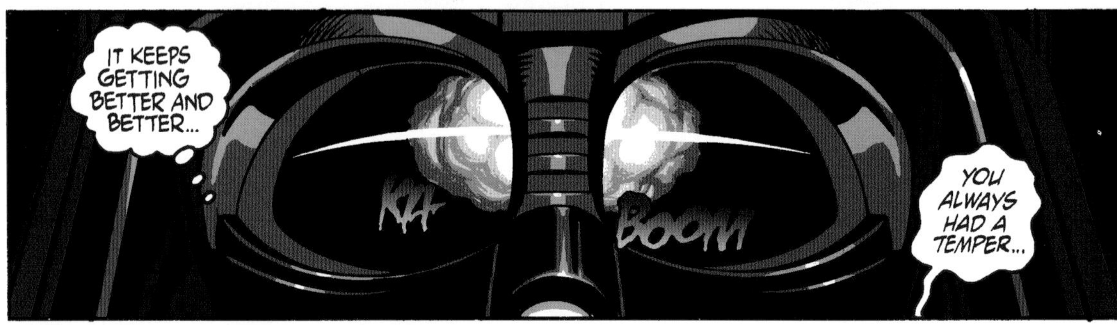
IT KEEPS GETTING BETTER AND BETTER...
KA-BOOM
YOU ALWAYS HAD A TEMPER...

THWACK
POP
MAYBE YOU SHOULD TRY YOUR LIGHT-SABER?
LORD VADER, THIS IS IMPERIAL DESTROYER XAMAURAL. DO YOU REQUIRE ASSISTANCE?

SIT UP STRAIGHT.

END

CALL ME SQUISHMAEL.
IT'S NOT MY REAL NAME, BUT MY REAL NAME COULD GET ME KILLED.
Y'SEE, I HAVE A BIG PROBLEM WITH SECRETS. I CAN'T KEEP 'EM. AND IN MY BUSINESS, THAT CAN MEAN AN EARLY RETIREMENT...
A FORCED RETIREMENT, IF YOU GET MY DRIFT.
STILL...YOU LOOK LIKE A TRUSTWORTHY SOUL, NOT THE KIND WHO WOULD RAT ME OUT, SO TODAY'S YOUR LUCKY DAY BECAUSE, FOR THE PRICE OF A DRINK, I'M GOING TO REVEAL TO YOU, FOR THE FIRST TIME EVER, THE TRUE AND COMPLETE STORY OF HAN SOLO'S...
KESSEL RUN!
YEAH, I KNOW...YOU'VE PROBABLY HEARD IT ALL...SPECULATIONS, RUMORS, EVEN OTHER VERSIONS OF THE TALE.
JUST ONE DRINK... HOW ABOUT IT?
WELL, FORGET ALL YOU'VE HEARD AND ALL YOU THINK YOU KNOW. I'VE GOT THE TRUE STORY, BECAUSE I WAS THERE THE NIGHT IT ALL STARTED...
"...THE NIGHT HAN SOLO WON THE MILLENNIUM FALCON!"
CONGRATULATIONS, HAN...THE FALCON IS YOURS.
THANKS, LANDO. MAN-OH-MAN, WHAT A NIGHT!

INDEED. YOU'RE IN THE BIG TIME, NOW, HAN M'BOY!
I GUESS I AM.
NOT SO FAST, HAN. IT TAKES MORE THAN A FAST SHIP TO BE A FIRST-CLASS SMUGGLER. IT TAKES A REPUTATION.
AND SHORT OF RUNNING GUNS TO CORUSCANT, THERE'S ONLY ONE WAY FOR A MAN OF YOUR LIMITED EXPERIENCE TO GET ON THE CHARTS.
YOU HAVE TO MAKE THE KESSEL RUN.
AH, YESSS...THE KESSEL RUN...
THE KESSEL RUN? WHAT'S THAT?
HA HA HA HA HA HA HA
YOURE AMONG FRIENDS, SO WE'LL PRETEND YOU DIDN'T SAY THAT, BUT...HEH HEH...OH, SET THIS BOY STRAIGHT, MARSHAK.
LET'S JUST SAY THIS... ANY SMUGGLER WHO HASN'T HEARD OF THE KESSEL RUN ISN'T WORTH A PILE OF BANTHA POODOO.
"I'D NEVER HEARD OF THE KESSEL RUN...BUT I DID KNOW WHAT BANTHA POODOO WAS."
HA HA! BANTHA POODOO... YUM.

I DIDN'T SAY I'D NEVER HEARD OF IT...I JUST NEVER LEARNED THE PARTICULARS, THAT'S ALL. TELL ME MORE.
I DUNNO...I DON'T THINK THE LAD'S UP TO IT, MARSHAK. HE'S PRETTY GREEN.
ACTUALLY, HE'S LOOKING PRETTY RED RIGHT NOW... ESPECIALLY HIS FACE.
SNICKER!
ALL RIGHT, ALL RIGHT, ENOUGH ALREADY! JUST FILL ME IN OR GET OFF MY SHIP!
OH-HO-HOOO! LISTEN TO THAT... "MY SHIP" ALREADY, HE SAYS!
THE INSOLENT PUP! HA HA HA!
IS IT MY SHIP...
...OR NOT?
SURE, IT'S YOUR SHIP. YOU WON HER FAIR AND SQUARE. BUT I LIKE YOU, HAN. AND MAYBE IF I DIDN'T, IF I WANTED REVENGE, I'D SEND YOU OUT ON THIS KESSEL RUN HOPING YOU'D GET BLASTED INTO A MILLION PIECES.
MAYBE PART OF ME WANTS THAT... BUT PART OF ME IS SORRY I BROUGHT IT UP.
LET'S JUST CALL IT A NIGHT, OKAY? FORGET I SAID ANYTHING.
C'MON, GUYS... SQUISHMAEL, MARSHAK...?

DELIGHTFUL EVENING, HAN. THANKS FOR THE SLIME--IT WAS DELICIOUS.
ECK.
LOOK, YOU CAN LEAVE IF YOU WANT, BUT ONE WAY OR ANOTHER, I'M GONNA MAKE THIS KESSEL RUN...
...WITH OR WITHOUT YOUR HELP.
"AND SO, AT HAN'S INSISTENCE, LANDO REVEALED TO US ALL THE SECRETS OF THE KESSEL RUN. HE PULLED UP A SCHEMATIC OF A SYSTEM WITH FIFTEEN PLANETS AND SHOWED IT TO HAN..."
HEY, WHAT DOES THAT DO?
LEAVE IT ALONE, SQUISH.
SO...THAT'S THE KESSEL SYSTEM.
OH, BOY.
WHAT A LASERBRAIN. IT'S NOT A SYSTEM... IT'S A BIRD.
A BIRD?!

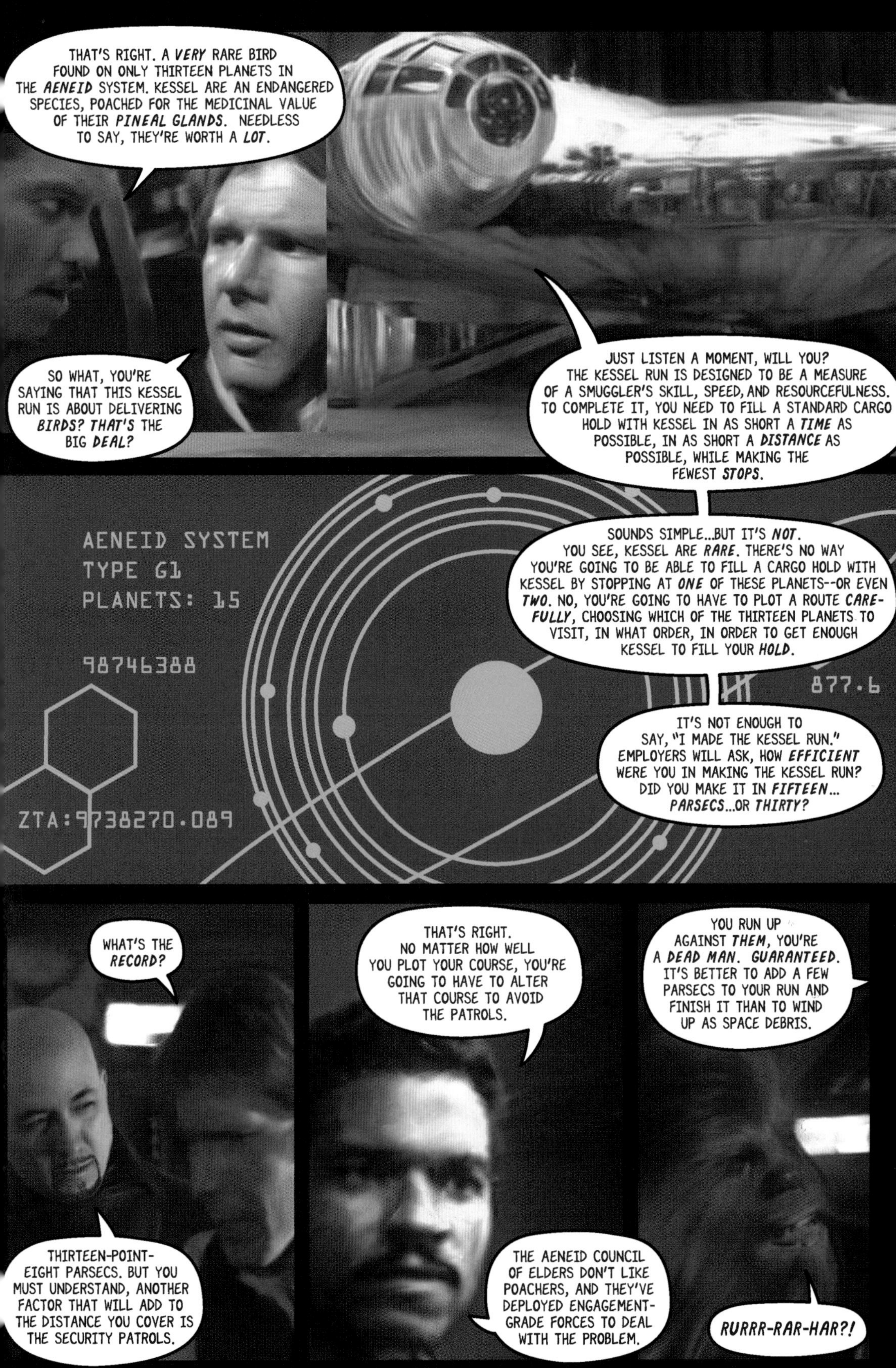
THAT'S RIGHT. A VERY RARE BIRD FOUND ON ONLY THIRTEEN PLANETS IN THE AENEID SYSTEM. KESSEL ARE AN ENDANGERED SPECIES, POACHED FOR THE MEDICINAL VALUE OF THEIR PINEAL GLANDS. NEEDLESS TO SAY, THEY'RE WORTH A LOT.
SO WHAT, YOU'RE SAYING THAT THIS KESSEL RUN IS ABOUT DELIVERING BIRDS? THAT'S THE BIG DEAL?
JUST LISTEN A MOMENT, WILL YOU? THE KESSEL RUN IS DESIGNED TO BE A MEASURE OF A SMUGGLER'S SKILL, SPEED, AND RESOURCEFULNESS. TO COMPLETE IT, YOU NEED TO FILL A STANDARD CARGO HOLD WITH KESSEL IN AS SHORT A TIME AS POSSIBLE, IN AS SHORT A DISTANCE AS POSSIBLE, WHILE MAKING THE FEWEST STOPS.
AENEID SYSTEM
TYPE G1
PLANETS: 15
98746388
ZTA:9738270.089
877.6
SOUNDS SIMPLE...BUT IT'S NOT. YOU SEE, KESSEL ARE RARE. THERE'S NO WAY YOU'RE GOING TO BE ABLE TO FILL A CARGO HOLD WITH KESSEL BY STOPPING AT ONE OF THESE PLANETS--OR EVEN TWO. NO, YOU'RE GOING TO HAVE TO PLOT A ROUTE CARE-FULLY, CHOOSING WHICH OF THE THIRTEEN PLANETS TO VISIT, IN WHAT ORDER, IN ORDER TO GET ENOUGH KESSEL TO FILL YOUR HOLD.
IT'S NOT ENOUGH TO SAY, "I MADE THE KESSEL RUN." EMPLOYERS WILL ASK, HOW EFFICIENT WERE YOU IN MAKING THE KESSEL RUN? DID YOU MAKE IT IN FIFTEEN... PARSECS...OR THIRTY?
WHAT'S THE RECORD?
THIRTEEN-POINT-EIGHT PARSECS. BUT YOU MUST UNDERSTAND, ANOTHER FACTOR THAT WILL ADD TO THE DISTANCE YOU COVER IS THE SECURITY PATROLS.
THAT'S RIGHT. NO MATTER HOW WELL YOU PLOT YOUR COURSE, YOU'RE GOING TO HAVE TO ALTER THAT COURSE TO AVOID THE PATROLS.
THE AENEID COUNCIL OF ELDERS DON'T LIKE POACHERS, AND THEY'VE DEPLOYED ENGAGEMENT-GRADE FORCES TO DEAL WITH THE PROBLEM.
YOU RUN UP AGAINST THEM, YOU'RE A DEAD MAN. GUARANTEED. IT'S BETTER TO ADD A FEW PARSECS TO YOUR RUN AND FINISH IT THAN TO WIND UP AS SPACE DEBRIS.
RURRR-RAR-HAR?!

THAT'S WHY I WISH YOU'D DROP THIS. YOU'RE NOT READY, HAN. YOU'RE A GOOD PILOT, BUT THIS ONE'S STRICTLY FOR THE BIG BOYS. WAIT A FEW YEARS, TILL YOU HAVE MORE EXPERIENCE, AND THEN MAYBE...
MAYBE NOTHING. MY LUCKY STREAK ISN'T OVER. I'M GONNA MAKE THIS KESSEL RUN ONE FOR THE BOOKS. YOU'LL SEE.
"SO WHEN WE LEFT THAT NIGHT, HAN WAS RESOLVED TO SET OUT THE NEXT MORNING FOR THE AENEID SYSTEM. HAN ALWAYS WAS A STUBBORN ONE, STUBBORN AND COCKY...AT LEAST, ON THE SURFACE..."
...I CAN'T BELIEVE IT...
'S HIS FUNERAL, I GUESS...
"BACK AT THE FALCON THAT NIGHT, IT WAS ANOTHER STORY..."
AW, HELL, CHEWIE... WHAT HAVE I GOTTEN MYSELF INTO?
HRRRARRR HUR RUR.
OKAY...US INTO?
I DON'T EVEN KNOW WHAT KESSEL LOOK LIKE. HOW DO YOU FIND THEM, MUCH LESS CATCH THEM?
ARRRRRR HARR HAR?
NO, I COULDN'T HAVE ASKED THEM ANY MORE QUESTIONS...THEY LAUGHED AT ME ENOUGH AS IT IS.
YRRRRWWW?
DON'T WORRY, PAL-- I'VE GOT A PLAN. YOU STAY HERE AND WATCH THE SHIP.
I'M GOING INTO TOWN TO DO SOME SERIOUS RESEARCH.

"OF COURSE, HAN'S RESEARCH MAINLY CONSISTED OF SEEING HOW MANY GLASSES OF *QUANYA* HE COULD TOSS BACK WHILE MAINTAINING CONTROL OF HIS *LEGS*. NEVER MUCH OF THE ACADEMIC, WAS HAN. HAN *HAD* BEEN RIGHT ABOUT *ONE* THING, THOUGH. HIS LUCKY STREAK *WASN'T* OVER. AS CHANCE WOULD HAVE IT, AFTER THE BAR HAD CLOSED AND HAN WAS DOWNING HIS LAST DRINK, DESTINY INTERVENED ONCE AGAIN, IN THE FORM OF A *MYSTERIOUS MESSENGER* WITH A *SHADY OFFER*..."
HAN SOLO?
WHO WANTS TO KNOW?
SOMEONE WHO WANTS TO HELP YOU FIND THE *FORTUNE AND GLORY* YOU *SEEK*.
WHAT DO *YOU* KNOW ABOUT WHAT *I'M* SEEKING?
I KNOW ONLY THAT YOU ARE ABOUT TO ATTEMPT THE *KESSEL RUN*...THE REST I *SURMISE*.

HOW DID YOU FIND OUT ABOUT THAT?
I OVERHEARD LANDO CALRISSIAN AND A BALD CORELLIAN DEBATING YOUR ODDS OF COMING OUT OF THIS ALIVE. CALRISSIAN SAID YOU WOULD BE DEAD BEFORE YOU HIT THE SIX-PARSEC MARK.
AND MARSHAK? THE CORELLIAN?
HE SAID FOUR PARSECS. PERSONALLY, I THINK YOU LOOK FAIRLY CAPABLE--AND WARRANT YOU MIGHT EVEN HIT NINE PARSECS BEFORE THE FLAMING END...IF YOU'RE CAREFUL.
OR...YOU CAN COMPLETE THE KESSEL RUN, WITHOUT A SCRATCH... AND IN RECORD TIME.
YOUR EXPLOIT WILL BECOME THE STUFF OF LEGEND, CAPTAIN SOLO. YOU WILL FINALLY BE THE PLAYER YOU'VE ALWAYS WANTED TO BE.
BUT IF YOU WANT THESE THINGS TO COME TO PASS... YOU HAVE TO TALK TO ME. NOW.
I'M LISTENING.
THIS DISK IS THE SOLUTION TO ALL YOUR PROBLEMS. IT CONTAINS THE NAMES AND COORDINATES OF THREE ASSOCIATES OF MINE, EACH STATIONED ON A DIFFERENT PLANET IN THE AENEID SYSTEM. BETWEEN THE THREE OF THEM, THEY IMMEDIATELY HAVE ENOUGH KESSEL ON HAND TO FILL YOUR HOLD.
FURTHERMORE, I HAVE CONNECTIONS WITHIN THE AENEID SECURITY FORCES. IN ADDITION TO THE NAMES OF THESE THREE MERCHANTS, THIS DISK ALSO CONTAINS A PRE-PLOTTED COURSE THAT WILL STEER YOU CLEAR OF ANY PATROLS IN THE SYSTEM.

THE COURSE ON THIS DISK WILL LEAD YOU TO THE THREE *PLANETS*...

...FILL YOUR *CARGO HOLD* WITH *KESSEL*, AND GET YOU OUT OF THE AENEID SYSTEM *INTACT*.

AND WHEN IT'S ALL DONE, YOU WILL BE THE *FIRST SMUGGLER* EVER TO COMPLETE THE *KESSEL RUN* IN LESS THAN TWELVE *PARSECS*.

SOUNDS TOO GOOD TO BE *TRUE*.

OH, IT'S TRUE... BUT THE DISK WILL COST YOU FIVE THOUSAND CREDITS.

*FIVE THOUSAND CREDITS?!* YOU'RE *INSANE!*

HMMM...PERHAPS YOU'D PREFER TO FUMBLE AROUND FOR *SIX MONTHS*, DODGING *PATROLS*, AND SEARCHING THE WOODS FOR KESSEL WITH A BIG *NET* AND A DRUKLOAD OF *BUG REPELLENT*.

OF COURSE, THAT MIGHT WORK FOR THE *LITTLE BUGS*... BUT THERE ARE SOME *MONSTERS* IN THOSE WOODS. THEY EAT KESSEL *AND* KESSEL HUNTERS WITH EQUAL ÉLAN. BUT EVEN SO, PERHAPS YOU PREFER SAVING SOME MONEY TO SAVING YOUR *LIFE*.

MAYBE I *WOULD*.
DO YOU KNOW WHAT A KESSEL *LOOKS* LIKE?
SURE. IT LOOKS LIKE A *BIRD*. YOU KNOW...FEATHERS...
DO YOU KNOW WHERE THEY *LIVE?*
*YEAH*. THEY LIVE IN THE *WOODS*.
AND YOU KNOW HOW TO *CATCH THEM*, DO YOU?
AW, COME *ON*...FIVE *THOUSAND?*
HOW DO I KNOW THIS IS ON THE *UP AND UP?*
BEING A PROFESSIONAL, I ANTICIPATED THAT QUESTION AND HAVE DEVISED A SOLUTION THAT PROTECTS US *BOTH*. THE DATA ON THIS DISK ARE ENCRYPTED IN MULTIPLE STAGES.
ONE THOUSAND CREDITS RIGHT *NOW* GETS YOU THE DISK, WHICH WILL TAKE YOU TO THE *FIRST* OF THE CONTACTS.
ONCE YOU HAVE SEEN THAT HE DOES INDEED HAVE THE KESSEL AS PROMISED, YOU WILL TRANSFER *ANOTHER* TWO THOUSAND INTO MY ACCOUNT, AND I WILL GIVE YOU THE NEXT ENCRYPTION KEY TO UNLOCK THE NEXT LEG OF YOUR JOURNEY.
ONCE THAT'S DONE, ONE ADDITIONAL TRANSFER OF TWO THOUSAND GETS YOU THE *FINAL PASSWORD*...AND A PLACE IN THE *HISTORY BOOKS*.
NOW TELL ME... IS THIS AN OFFER YOU CAN AFFORD TO *REFUSE*...?

IT WASN'T.
HAN FORKED OVER THE CREDITS AND RAN BACK TO THE *FALCON*, BURSTING TO MAKE HIS MARK ON THE UNSUSPECTING UNIVERSE...WITH A LITTLE BIT OF *ILLICIT HELP*.
NOT AN HOUR LATER, *HAN* AND *CHEWIE* BLASTED OFF FROM *TATOOINE*...
...MADE THE JUMP TO *HYPERSPACE*...
...AND EMERGED IN THE *AENEID SYSTEM*, DIRECTLY IN ORBIT AROUND THEIR FIRST DESTINATION.
"THE *KESSEL RUN* HAD *BEGUN*.

"THEY KILLED THEIR LANDING FLOODS AND PUT DOWN AT THE FAR END OF THE AGRICULTURAL COMPOUND, JUST AS DIRECTED..."

ZZZZT!

WHADDYA *WANT?*
HAN SOLO. I BELIEVE YOU'RE EXPECTING ME.

*FINALLY*. I'VE GOT YOUR *MERCHANDISE* ALL READY. I WANT 'EM OUT OF HERE BEFORE *SUNRISE*.

YOU AND ME *BOTH*, OLD MAN. I GOT A *RUN* TO FINISH.
JUST MAKE SURE NO ONE SEES YOU *LOADING* THEM. I'M TAKING AN AWFUL RISK. HANDLING ITEMS THIS HOT MAKES ME *NERVOUS*.

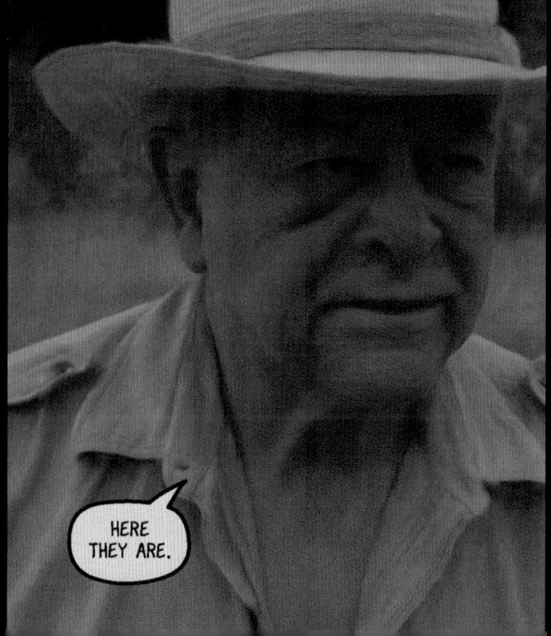
HERE THEY ARE.

SQUARK
SQUARK SQUARK
SQUARK
*THOSE* ARE *KESSEL?! THOSE* ARE WORTH A *FORTUNE?*
YOU GOT IT, CAP...ONLY I AIN'T GONNA *CHARGE* YOU A FORTUNE, ON ACCOUNT OF I GOTTA GET *RID* OF 'EM. NO, I'M *ONLY* GONNA CHARGE YOU...THREE THOUSAND.

THREE *THOUSAND? CREDITS?*
DAMN *RIGHT*, CREDITS! YOU KNOW HOW MUCH YOU CAN *GET* FOR THESE THINGS ON *RANGORAH?*
NO...I WAS TOLD TO DELIVER THESE TO *FONKER DAHK* AT THE *EVENT HORIZON* ON RANGORAH, BUT THE *PRICE*...

WHAT KIND OF SMUGGLER *ARE* YOU? LET ME JUST SAY THIS...IF YOU TAKE LESS THAN TWELVE THOUSAND FOR THIS BUNCH, YOU'RE A *FOOL*.
SQUARK

OH, *YEAH?* BUT YOU'RE WILLING TO SETTLE FOR THREE. DOES THAT MAKE *YOU* A FOOL?
*MWARRRRH MOW MOW?*
NO, A *COWARD*. YOU WANT 'EM OR *NOT?*

SQUARK?
SQUARK!
@$#!!
"SO *HAN PUSHED* AND *CHEWIE PULLED*...WHAT ELSE COULD THEY *DO?*

"THE FIRST PART OF HIS RUN COMPLETE, HAN CONTACTED THE MYSTERIOUS ALIEN FOR FURTHER INSTRUCTIONS..."

I TRUST THE TRANSACTION WENT DOWN WITHOUT INCIDENT...?

YEAH, JUST LIKE YOU ***SAID***. I WANT THE NEXT ENCRYPTION KEY.

TWO THOUSAND CREDITS AND IT'S ***YOURS***.

THE TRANSFER IS ***COMPLETE***.

YES...I'M TRANSMITTING THE CODE ***NOW***. GOOD ***HUNTING***, SOLO.

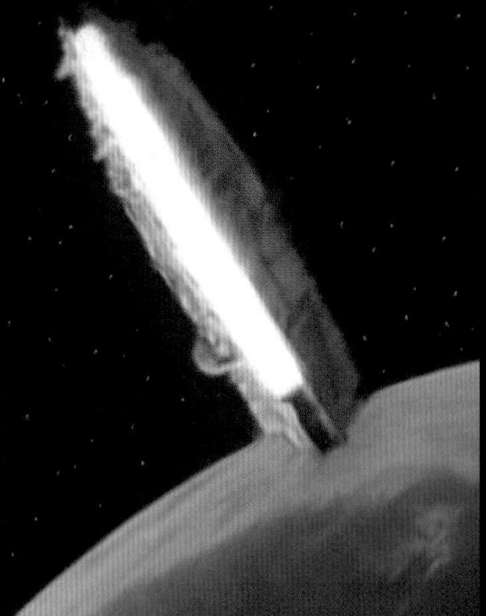

"EXACTLY AS PROMISED, THEY ARRIVED AT THE SECOND RENDEZVOUS WITHOUT ENCOUNTERING RESISTANCE OF ANY KIND.

"THEY FOUND THE SECOND MERCHANT AS EXPECTED...WHAT ***WASN'T*** EXPECTED WAS THE ***PRICE...FIVE THOUSAND CREDITS!***"

"SO ANYWAY, WHEN HAN HOOKED UP WITH THE FINAL MERCHANT, HE GOT A VERY NASTY SURPRISE..."
SEVEN THOUSAND.
S-SEVEN...? ARE YOU OUT OF YOUR MIND?
TAKE IT OR LEAVE IT, PAL.
SIGH.
"SO THINK ABOUT IT...IF YOU DO THE MATH, THIS KESSEL RUN HAD NOW COST HAN ELEVEN THOUSAND CREDITS...PLUS TWO THOUSAND FOR THE FINAL ENCRYPTION KEY. STILL, THE PATH TO FORTUNE AND GLORY IS NOT WITHOUT A FEW BUMPS, EH? (YOU GOT ANY SALTED NUTS? I'M A LITTLE HUNGRY.)
"WHAT ELSE COULD HE DO? HE HADN'T COME THIS FAR TO FAIL...AND BY THE WAY, I'M GETTING AWFUL DRY...HOW ABOUT ANOTHER DRINK? JUST ONE? AHHHH...THAT'LL DO IT. MANY THANKS. SO ANYWAY, HAN PAID UP, AND THIS OLD CUSS LED HAN AND CHEWIE OVER TO A LARGE PEN..."
THERE YOU GO. HELP YOURSELVES.
WHADDYA MEAN? THEY'RE RUNNING LOOSE! CAN'T YOU PUT THEM IN A CRATE FOR US?
NAH. I'D NEVER BE ABLE TO CATCH THEM. THEY'RE FAST, AND THEY HAVE A NASTY PECK...THAT'S A REAL TOUGH JOB. I'D NEVER HAVE A CHANCE.
HAVE FUN, KIDS! HEH HEH HEH...

WELL, FRIEND, I'M HERE TO TELL YOU THEY HAD ONE HELL OF A TIME ROUNDING UP THOSE BIRDS. IF YOU'LL FORGIVE THE PUN... THOSE KESSEL RUN!
AND SO, SCRATCHED, BRUISED, AND RUFFLED, ONE STANDARD CARGO HOLD FILLED WITH KESSEL, AND 17,000 CREDITS LIGHTER OF POCKET, HAN AND CHEWIE HEADED FOR RANGORAH, THE KESSEL RUN COMPLETE... AT 11.8 PARSECS!
I'M A LEGEND NOW.
MARFHH!
OKAY...WE'RE LEGENDS NOW.
HAN AND CHEWIE WERE SUPPOSED TO REPORT TO FONKER DAHK AT THE EVENT HORIZON, A POPULAR BAR ON RANGORAH.
"DAHK, A PROMINENT FIGURE IN THE SMUGGLER UNDERGROUND, WOULD BOTH PAY HAN FOR THE KESSEL AND REVIEW HIS FLIGHT LOG TO CONFIRM THE RUN.
"NOT KNOWING WHAT DAHK LOOKED LIKE, HAN FOLLOWED A TIME-HONORED TRADITION. HE ASKED THE BARTENDER..."
I'M LOOKING FOR FONKER DAHK.
THAT'S ME.
A BARTENDER, HUH? GOOD COVER.
WELL, DAHK, BREAK OPEN THE HISTORY BOOKS. YOU'RE LOOKING AT THE MAN WHO JUST MADE THE KESSEL RUN IN LESS THAN TWELVE PARSECS!

YOU MADE THE KESSEL RUN?
IN LESS THAN TWELVE PARSECS.
HEY, EVERYBODY! LISTEN UP!
WE GOT ANOTHER KESSEL RUNNER!
HA HA! HEY...ANYBODY WANNA BUY A KESSEL?!
HA
HA
HA
OH, BROTHER... HA HA HA!
UH-OH.
HA
HA
HA
BEEP BEEP BEEP!
SSS SSS SSS!
HEH HEH HEH!
DAMN.
LOOKS LIKE WE REALLY BLEW IT THIS TIME, CHEWIE...
ER...CHEWIE?
HA
HA
HA
HA
"MEANWHILE, OUTSIDE..."
CHUF HARF HARF!*
HEH HEH!
* TRANSLATION: "HEY... DID'JA SEE THAT GUY? HE MADE THE KESSEL RUN!"

"THE NEXT DAY, SEVERAL LIGHT YEARS AWAY, THE CONSPIRATORS DIVVIED UP THEIR ILL-GOTTEN GAINS..."
OKAY, LET'S FINISH UP AND HIT THE CASINO. THERE'S GAMBLING TO BE DONE!
OH, MAN, I WISH I COULD'VE SEEN HAN'S FACE WHEN HE FOUND OUT THOSE BIRDS ARE WORTH NOTHING!
NAHHH...I HATED TO PULL THAT OLD KESSEL SCAM ON POOR HAN...BUT, HEY, AT LEAST WE GOT BACK THE MONEY WE LOST TO HIM!
AND THEN SOME!
DON'T WORRY, MARSHAK...I TAPED THEM CHASING THOSE KESSEL. IT WAS GREAT.
I'LL SHOW YOU THE HOLO...FOR A REASONABLE PRICE...!
SIGH.
YEAH, THAT'S RIGHT. KESSEL ARE ABSOLUTELY WORTHLESS. THEY'RE SO COMMON, THEY'RE CONSIDERED VERMIN BY FARMERS IN EIGHT DIFFERENT SYSTEMS. IN FACT, THEY'RE NOT CALLED KESSEL AT ALL. THAT'S JUST A NAME THEY MADE UP SO THE SUCKERS COULDN'T LOOK THEM UP IN DATABASES.
AND SO, THAT'S THE COMPLETE AND TRUE STORY OF HAN SOLO'S KESSEL RUN. LANDO GOT REVENGE ON HAN FOR WINNING HIS SHIP, AND HAN, EVER RESOURCEFUL, WOULD PROUDLY MENTION MAKING THE KESSEL RUN IN LESS THAN TWELVE PARSECS TO ANY RUBE WHO QUESTIONED HIS CREDENTIALS, MAKING HUBBA OUT OF HUBBESS, SO TO SPEAK. PRETTY FUNNY, EH? OF COURSE, HAN LATER GOT HIS OWN REVENGE...BUT THAT'S ANOTHER STORY. AND DON'T FEEL TOO SORRY FOR HAN...HE WAS CHEATING AT SABACC WHEN HE WON THE FALCON. AH, WELL, BOYS WILL BE BOYS, HEH HEH HEH...
WHAT'S THAT, YOU SAY? I'M FULL OF BANTHA POODOO? I WISH! BUT, HEY, TAKE MY STORY OR LEAVE IT--WHAT DO I CARE? I KNOW THERE ARE THOSE WHO SAY DIFFERENT ABOUT THE KESSEL RUN, AND YES, WE SLOOGARIANS ARE KNOWN TO PLAY LOOSE WITH THE TRUTH SOMETIMES, BUT YOU SHOULD'VE THOUGHT OF THAT BEFORE YOU GAVE ME THOSE DRINKS. ALL I CAN SAY IS, THEY GOT THEIR STORY AND I GOT MINE.
BELIEVE WHAT YOU WANT... ALTHOUGH FOR THE PRICE OF ONE MORE DRINK, I'LL TELL YOU ABOUT THE TIME ME AND MY GOOD BUDDY DARTH VADER WENT TAUNTAUN BUSTING ON HOTH...!
END!

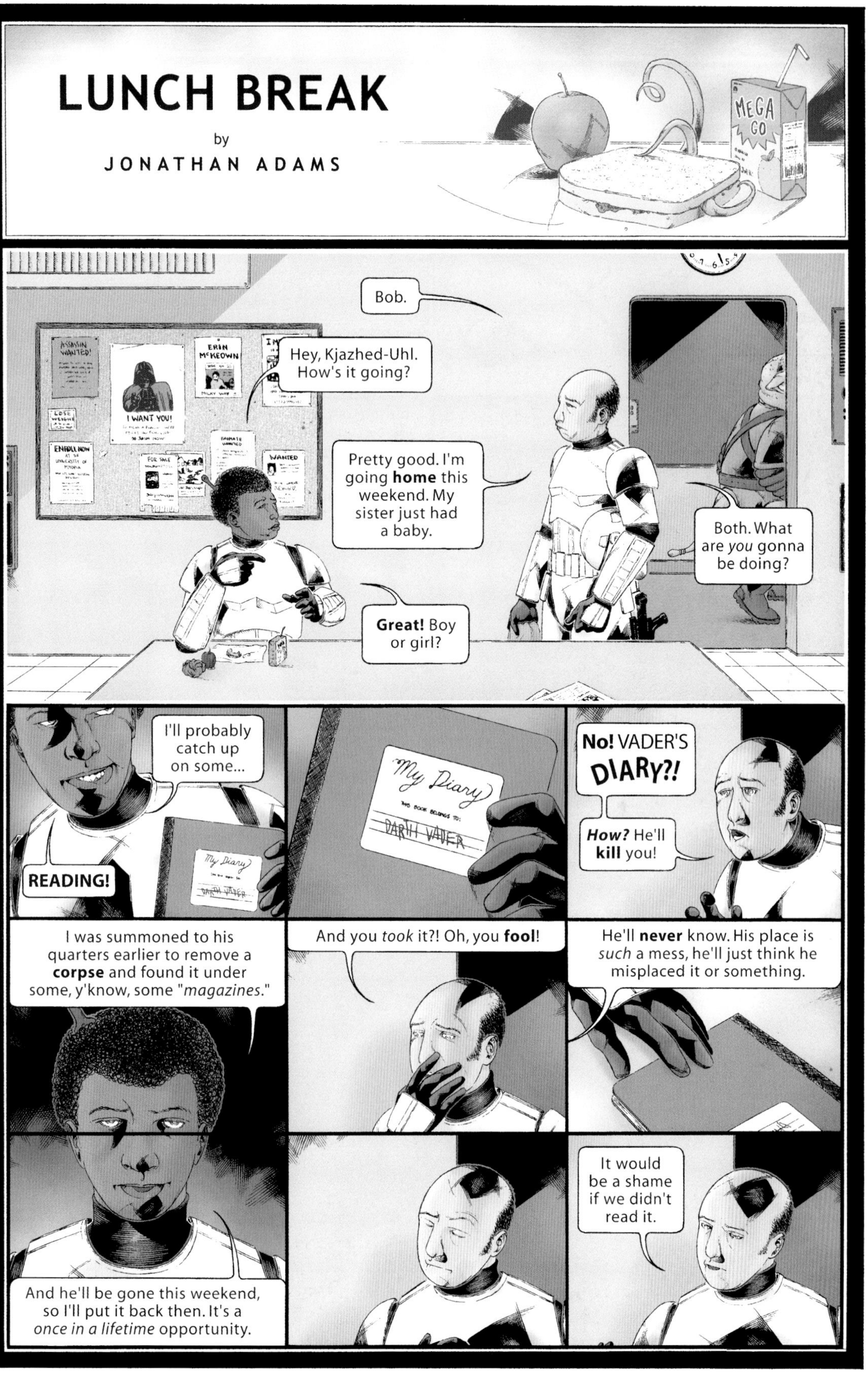

# LUNCH BREAK

by

JONATHAN ADAMS

Bob.

Hey, Kjazhed-Uhl. How's it going?

Pretty good. I'm going **home** this weekend. My sister just had a baby.

**Great!** Boy or girl?

Both. What are *you* gonna be doing?

I'll probably catch up on some...

**READING!**

My Diary

DARTH VADER

**No!** VADER'S DIARY?!

*How?* He'll **kill** you!

I was summoned to his quarters earlier to remove a **corpse** and found it under some, y'know, some "*magazines*."

And you *took* it?! Oh, you **fool**!

He'll **never** know. His place is *such* a mess, he'll just think he misplaced it or something.

And he'll be gone this weekend, so I'll put it back then. It's a *once in a lifetime* opportunity.

It would be a shame if we didn't read it.

Let's see here...
Got a new helmet today! A better fit than the last, and I don't get so hot and sweaty. Plus, it looks a bit more menacing. Not much time to write. I have to be up early for a meeting tomorrow. I'm sick of meetings. I just want to get out and do some evil. I haven't been sleeping well, lots of nitemares...
He misspelled nightmare.
No.
It's one of those words you can spell either way.
Like *nucular.*
Okay. Why don't we just skip to something ***else***?
Ummm... Here we go.
It's going to happen soon, I'm sure of it. I'm going to meet Luke Skywalker, and I'll have to tell him I'm his father. I'm not sure how I'll say it. Maybe something like: "Do I seem familiar at all?" or "Hey, me and your mom used to date." Perhaps it would be best to be straightforward and say, "Look, I am your father." The worst thing is, I'm not sure how he'll react. If he even believes me, that is. Which seems doubtful. I mean, what are the odds that his arch nemesis would wind up being his dad? He has so much anger towards me as is, this would only compound matters.

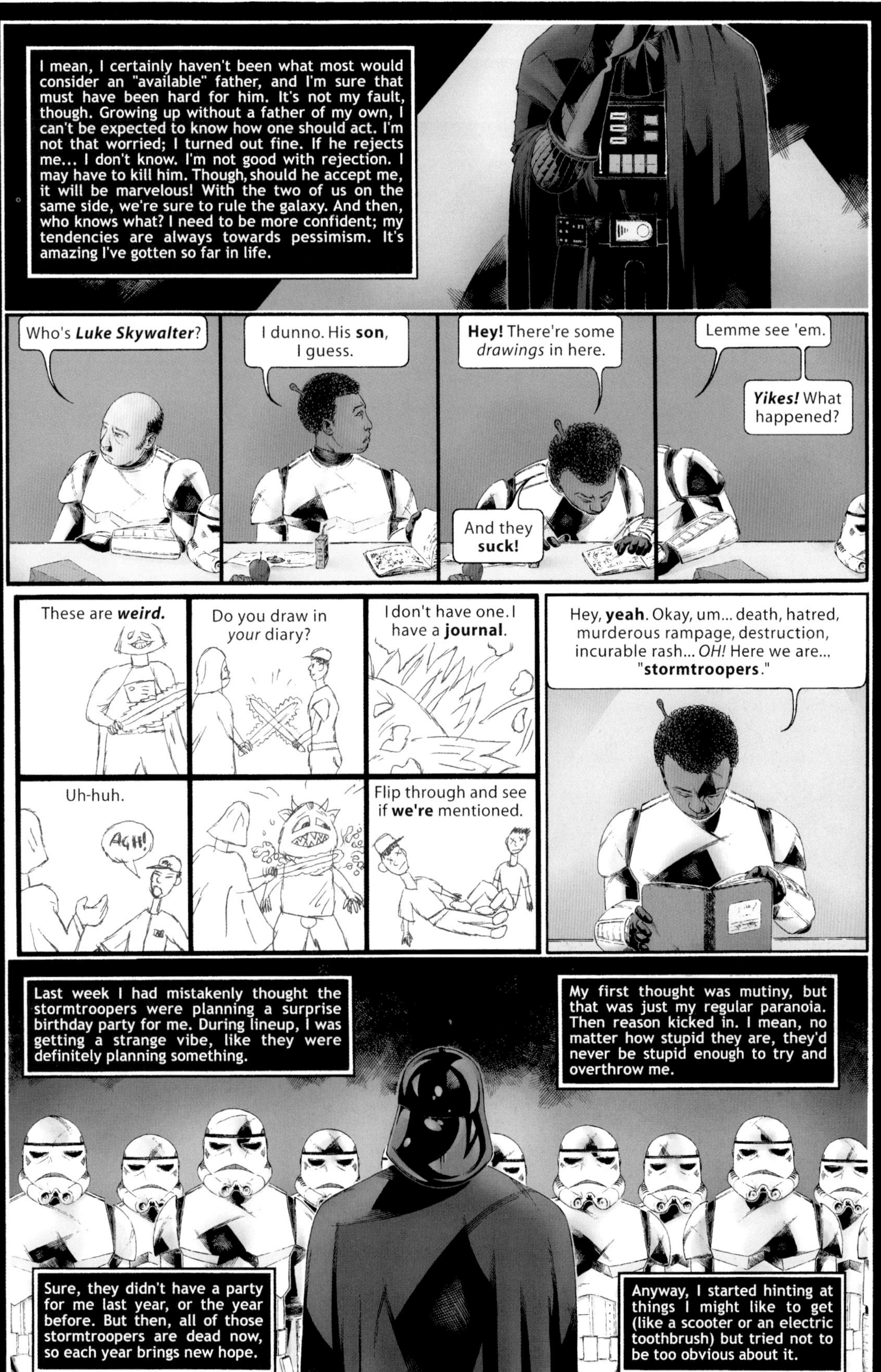
I mean, I certainly haven't been what most would consider an "available" father, and I'm sure that must have been hard for him. It's not my fault, though. Growing up without a father of my own, I can't be expected to know how one should act. I'm not that worried; I turned out fine. If he rejects me... I don't know. I'm not good with rejection. I may have to kill him. Though, should he accept me, it will be marvelous! With the two of us on the same side, we're sure to rule the galaxy. And then, who knows what? I need to be more confident; my tendencies are always towards pessimism. It's amazing I've gotten so far in life.
Who's ***Luke Skywalter***?
I dunno. His **son**, I guess.
**Hey!** There're some *drawings* in here.
And they **suck!**
Lemme see 'em.
***Yikes!*** What happened?
These are ***weird.***
Do you draw in *your* diary?
I don't have one. I have a **journal**.
Uh-huh.
AGH!
Flip through and see if **we're** mentioned.
Hey, **yeah**. Okay, um... death, hatred, murderous rampage, destruction, incurable rash... *OH!* Here we are... "**stormtroopers**."
Last week I had mistakenly thought the stormtroopers were planning a surprise birthday party for me. During lineup, I was getting a strange vibe, like they were definitely planning something.
My first thought was mutiny, but that was just my regular paranoia. Then reason kicked in. I mean, no matter how stupid they are, they'd never be stupid enough to try and overthrow me.
Sure, they didn't have a party for me last year, or the year before. But then, all of those stormtroopers are dead now, so each year brings new hope.
Anyway, I started hinting at things I might like to get (like a scooter or an electric toothbrush) but tried not to be too obvious about it.

Finally, last night (my birthday), my presence was urgently requested in a meeting room. When I got there, I drew my breath in, opened the door, and prepared to be surprised.
Only General Chymoelaan was in the room.
I looked around, curious as to where everybody was hiding. Were they to burst forth from behind a door at some point? No. By the time the meeting adjourned, it seemed...
nobody was hiding
at all.
Walking back to my quarters, craving my imminent solitude, I passed a room wherein several stormtroopers had gathered. They were laughing, eating cake, and wearing party hats. How grotesque. It was a surprise party after all, but not for me. It would seem one of the stormtroopers and I share the same birthday. Mental note: kill him.
I stepped into the room, though I'm not sure why. Instantly, they all froze, just staring at me like zombies.
As so often happens, my domineering presence led me to be ostracized.
I turned and left.
Again, it seemed, I'd been forgotten. In the end, however, I will surely be remembered!!! My accomplishments will long outlive this body, and my name will be known to all. And all will fear it! Unfortunately, I could not keep such uplifting thoughts in mind. The depression hit me so quickly this time that not even halfway back to my quarters, all I wanted to do was sleep. Though I suspect that this was partly due to the fact that I'd been up for 3 days straight. I do tend to work myself too hard, but that's just how passionate I am about my work.
I've always put work before myself.

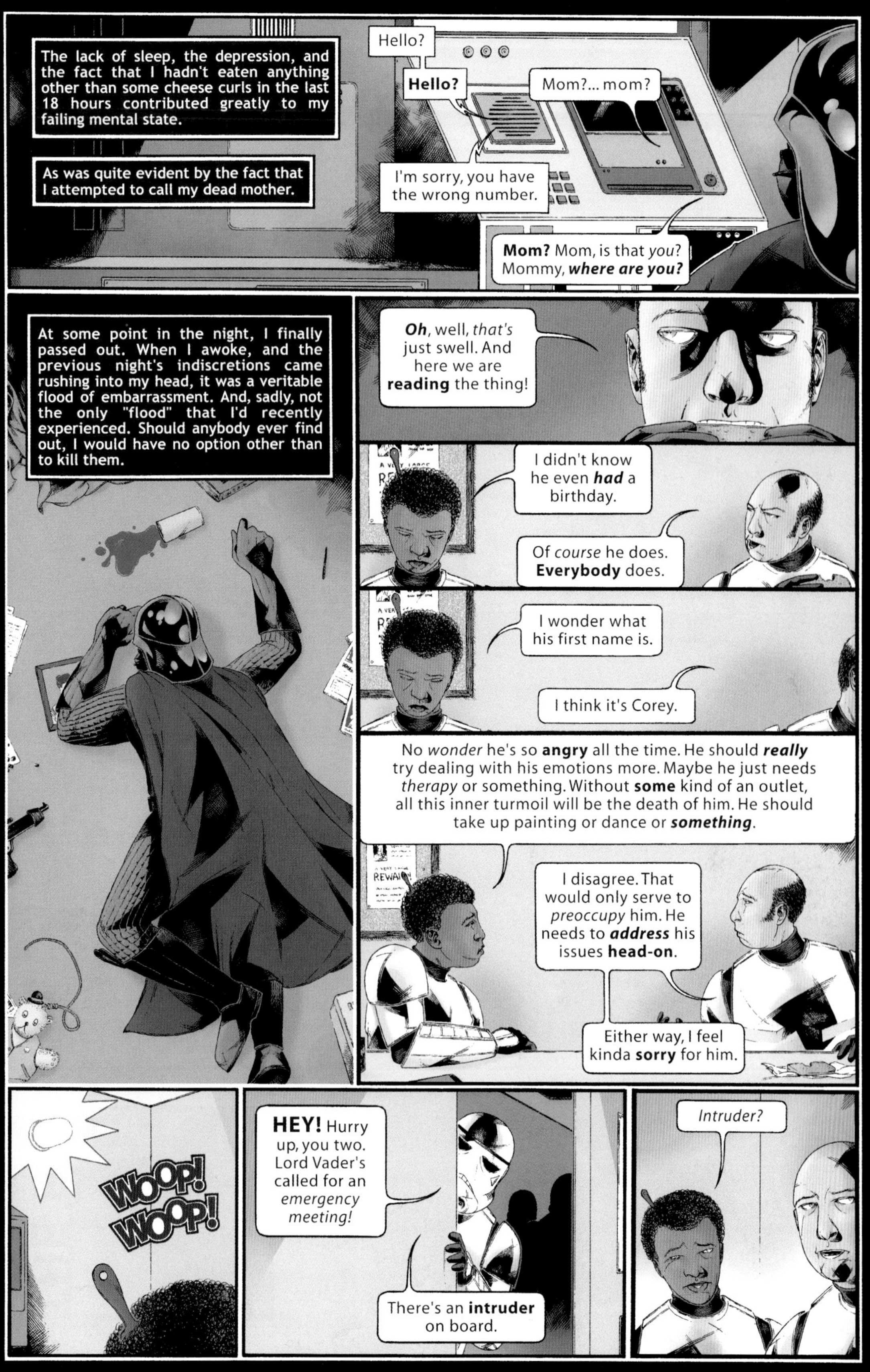
The lack of sleep, the depression, and the fact that I hadn't eaten anything other than some cheese curls in the last 18 hours contributed greatly to my failing mental state.
As was quite evident by the fact that I attempted to call my dead mother.
Hello?
Hello?
Mom?... mom?
I'm sorry, you have the wrong number.
Mom? Mom, is that you? Mommy, where are you?
At some point in the night, I finally passed out. When I awoke, and the previous night's indiscretions came rushing into my head, it was a veritable flood of embarrassment. And, sadly, not the only "flood" that I'd recently experienced. Should anybody ever find out, I would have no option other than to kill them.
Oh, well, that's just swell. And here we are reading the thing!
I didn't know he even had a birthday.
Of course he does. Everybody does.
I wonder what his first name is.
I think it's Corey.
No wonder he's so angry all the time. He should really try dealing with his emotions more. Maybe he just needs therapy or something. Without some kind of an outlet, all this inner turmoil will be the death of him. He should take up painting or dance or something.
I disagree. That would only serve to preoccupy him. He needs to address his issues head-on.
Either way, I feel kinda sorry for him.
WOOP! WOOP!
HEY! Hurry up, you two. Lord Vader's called for an emergency meeting!
There's an intruder on board.
Intruder?

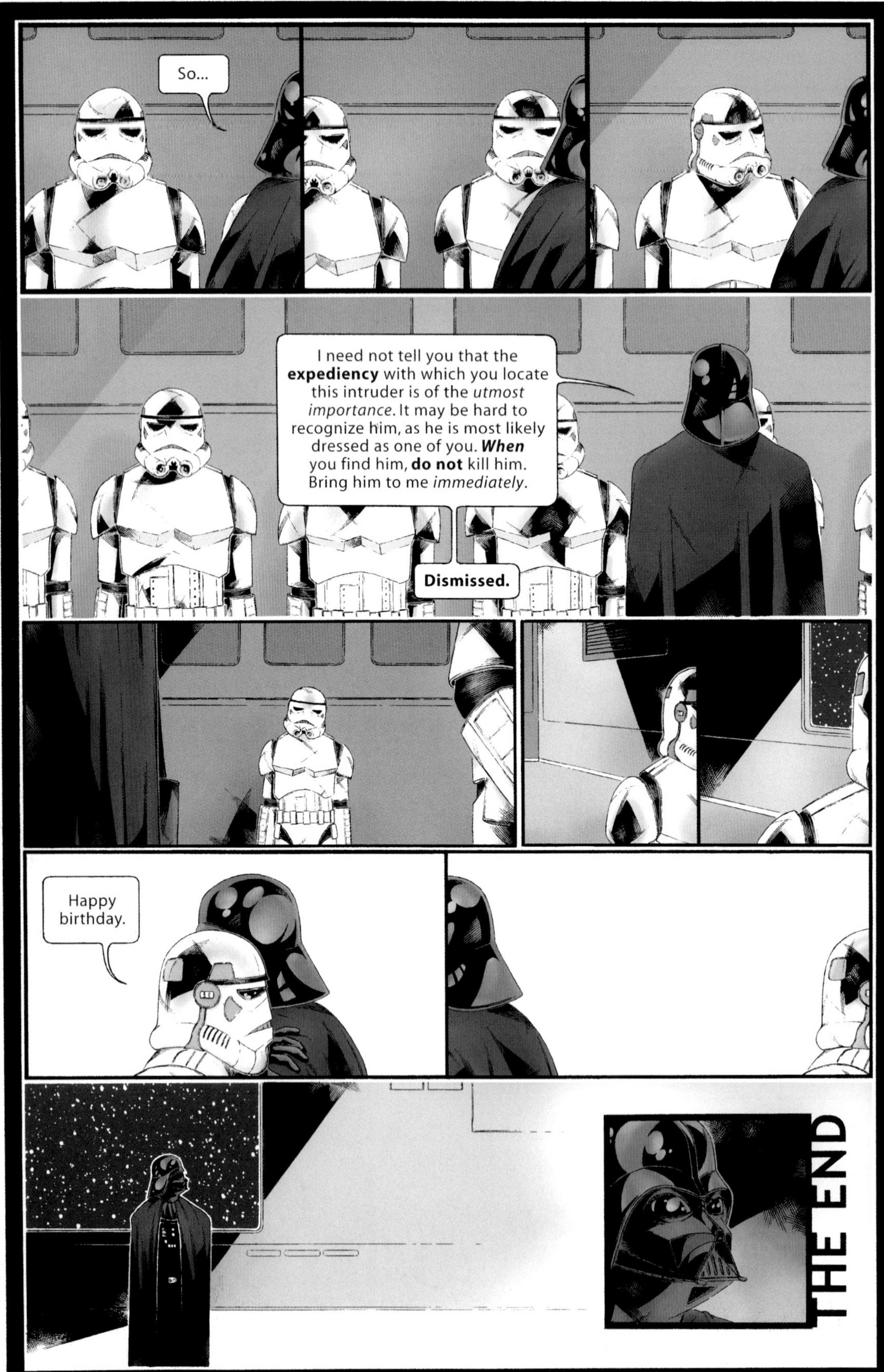
So...
I need not tell you that the **expediency** with which you locate this intruder is of the *utmost importance*. It may be hard to recognize him, as he is most likely dressed as one of you. ***When*** you find him, **do not** kill him. Bring him to me *immediately*.
**Dismissed.**
Happy birthday.
THE END

HEART OF DARKNESS
SEVEN HUNDRED YEARS BEFORE THE BATTLE OF YAVIN, THE COUNCIL HAS SENT A GROUP OF JEDI KNIGHTS TO STOP A DARK JEDI, CUTTING A SWATH OF DESTRUCTION THROUGH THE BPFASSHI STAR SYSTEM.
THE PURSUIT HAS LED THEM TO A COMMERCE GUILD TRADING STATION.

I HAVE ONE, LEVEL FIVE, SECTION D. TELL CONTROL TO SEAL THE BULKHEAD DOOR.
THERE IS NO ESCAPE. CORNERED, YOU ARE.

YOU THINK YOU CAN STOP ME?

WHY DON'T YOU RUN ALONG HOME AND MEDITATE BEFORE YOU GET HURT.
KKRRRAAACCKK

THE COUNCIL MUST BE DESPERATE TO SEND PADAWANS AFTER US.
A JEDI *KNIGHT,* I AM.

FORESEE THE FUTURE. THE DAYS OF THE JEDI ARE NUMBERED. THE LEGIONS OF BPFASSHI GROWS. YOU CANNOT DEFEAT US ALL.
DEFEAT YOU, WE HAVE. DEFEAT YOU...I *WILL.*

BIG TALK, LITTLE ONE.

VWOOM
OOOF!

DON'T WORRY, MINCH, WE'VE GOT IT.
SURRENDER, DARK SIDER. WE HAVE YOU OUT-NUMBERED.

WHERE IS YOUR MASTER?

YOU HAVE WON THIS TIME, JEDI...

...BUT I WILL TELL YOU *NOTHING!*
SSHHRAAKKLL

A PITY. SUCH IS THE FATE OF ALL WHO EMBRACE THE DARK SIDE.
MASTER T'DAI, THIS IS THE *TAKARA.*

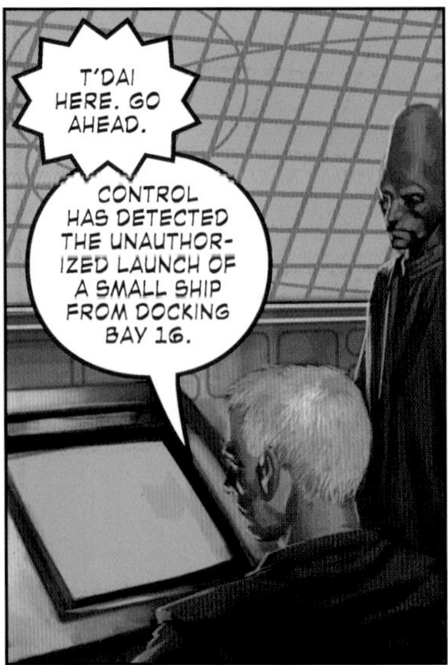
T'DAI HERE. GO AHEAD.
CONTROL HAS DETECTED THE UNAUTHOR-IZED LAUNCH OF A SMALL SHIP FROM DOCKING BAY 16.

WHY WASN'T THAT BAY LOCKED DOWN?
APPARENTLY, THE CONTROLS WERE OVER-RIDDEN.

IT MUST BE THE BPFASSHI MASTER.
TO YOUR SHIPS.

NO RESPONSE TO OUR HAILS.
HE'S HEADING TOWARD THE SLUIS SECTOR.

BPFASSHI SHIP--CUT YOUR ENGINES AND PREPARE TO BE TOWED.
HE'S MAKING A RUN FOR IT TOWARD THAT PLANET.

SETTING COURSE FOR PURSUIT. ESCAPING HE IS.

STAND DOWN, MINCH.
NAV COM SAYS IT'S DAGOBAH. NO TECHNOLOGY, MASSIVE LIFE-FORM READINGS, STRONG STORMS IN THE UPPER ATMOS-PHERE.
LANDING WOULD BE TOO DANGEROUS IN SMALL SHIPS. WE'LL REMAIN IN ORBIT AND WAIT FOR THE *TAKARA* TO ARRIVE.

TOO SMALL, YOU THINK I AM. PURSUE, I WILL. THERE IS NO FEAR, ONLY COURAGE.
MINCH! RETURN TO FORMATION!

A MESS, IT IS DOWN HERE. I AM FOLLOWING THE BPFASSHI'S ION TRAIL.

KRAKOOOM

BWOOOP
BWOOOP
BWOOOP
DISABLED, MY AFT THRUSTERS. EMERGENCY LANDING PROCEDURES INITIATED.

KRASH
SPOOOSH

I'VE LANDED. MY SHIP IS IN BAD SHAPE.
SIT TIGHT, MINCH. WE HAVE YOUR COORDINATES. THE *TAKARA* WILL BE HERE IN A PARSEC.
WAIT--DARKNESS I SENSE. NEARBY HE IS.
SIT TIGHT, MINCH!

SHOW YOURSELF, BPFASSHI. I KNOW YOU ARE...

...THERE!

ARRGH!!
THE VEGETATION IS TOO DENSE.

SCHWOM

SSSHHHRRAAAKKK

HE IS NEAR...

SURRENDER, YOU MUST. YOUR MINIONS HAVE FALLEN. FAILED YOU HAVE.

I THINK NOT. THERE ARE ALWAYS MORE TO BE TURNED.
PERHAPS YOU.

A JEDI, I AM. MY PATH IS WITH THE FORCE.
A JEDI? YOU ARE BUT A CHILD-- SMALL AND WEAK, FULL OF FEAR AND ANGER.

I AM NOT A CHILD!

SIZE MATTERS NOT.
BRRREKKJZZ

WHHOOOMMMKRCKLLLL
FOOLISH JEDI. AS YOU SEE...

...SIZE DOES MATTER!

AARGGHH!

CUT YOU DOWN, I WILL!
KRRRCHKKSSH

YOU CANNOT WIN. IF YOU STRIKE ME DOWN...

...I SHALL BECOME MORE POWERFUL!
SSSHHHVOOOMMM

UNNH--!
FEAR NOT, LITTLE ONE. GIVE INTO THE DARK SIDE, AND I WILL SHOW YOU WHAT TRUE POWER IS.

WHU--?

EVEN IF YOU STRIKE ME DOWN...

...KNOW THAT I HAVE DEFEATED YOU. YOUR MIND IS WEAK. OPEN AS A BOOK, WRITTEN WITH FEAR AND ANGER.
...UNNNHHH...

THERE IS YET HOPE FOR YOU...

...YOU WILL MAKE A GREAT ADDITION... TO THE DARK JEDI...ONE DAY...

MINCH, THE *TAKARA* HAS ARRIVED. WE ARE LANDING NOW. REPORT.

DEAD IS THE BPFASSHI MASTER. COMPLETE IS OUR MISSION.
WE ARE SETTING DOWN IN A CLEARING NEAR YOUR LOCATION. PREPARE TO RECEIVE THE COORDI-NATES.

AWAY FROM THIS CURSED PLACE, THE SOONER THE BETTER.
*ON THIS FATEFUL DAY, ON THIS REMOTE PLANET, FOREVER IS CHANGED THE BALANCE OF THE FORCE.*
*A NEW PLACE OF POWER, ANNOINTED WITH THE SWEAT OF THE JUST AND THE BLOOD OF THE WICKED, IS FOUNDED.*
THE END

Star Wars: Tales #13 / COVER BY TIM BRADSTREET

**Star Wars: Tales #14** / COVER BY PAT LEE

Star Wars: Tales #15 / COVER BY LEINIL FRANCIS YU

**Star Wars: Tales #16** / COVER BY ASHLEY WOOD